INSIDE STORIES I

SECOND EDITION

Edited by
GLEN KIRKLAND
RICHARD DAVIES

Thomson Nelson, 1120 Birchmount Road, Toronto, ON, M1K 5G4
www.nelson.com

Canadian Cataloguing in Publication Data

Main entry under title:

Inside stories I
2nd ed
ISBN-13 : 978-0-7747-0581-3.
ISBN-10 : 0-7747-0581-7

1. Short stories, Canadian (English).* 2. Short stories, American.
3. Short stories, English. I. Kirkland, Glen. II. Davies, Richard.

PN6120.2.I58 1999 823'.0108 C99-930536-0

About the Editors

Glen Kirkland
Glen is the Secondary English Consultant (Grades 7–12) for the English Catholic Schools in Edmonton, Alberta. Originally from McLennan, Alberta, Glen is well-known for his many inservices and workshops. An educator, editor, and writer, Glen leads an active life in education and communications.

Richard Davies
An English teacher at Strathcona High School for the Edmonton Public Schools, Richard is co-author of 35 publications with Glen Kirkland. Originally from Winnipeg, Manitoba, Richard combines writing, editing, and performing with his teaching career.

Project Manager: Gaynor Fitzpatrick
Developmental Editor: Lou Fletcher
Editorial Assistant: Ian Nussbaum
Production Editor: Jinnean Barnard
Production Coordinator: Tanya Mossa
Copy Editor: Sharlene Weaver
Permissions Coordinator: Patricia Buckley
Permissions Editor: Mary Rose MacLachlan
Photo Research: Maria DeCambra
Cover and Interior Design: Sonya V. Thursby/Opus House
Page Composition: Carolyn Hutchings
Cover Illustration: José Ortega/The Stock Illustration Source
Printing and Binding: Transcontinental Printing Limited

Printed in Canada
4 5 08 07 06

For our mothers, with love and gratitude—
Carmeline Kirkland and Rosalie Davies

G.K.
R.D.

Table of Contents

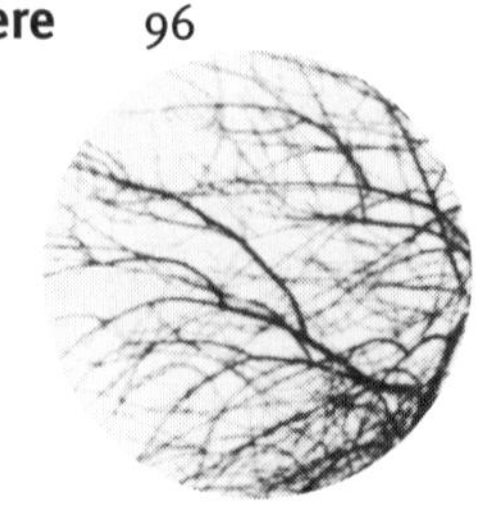

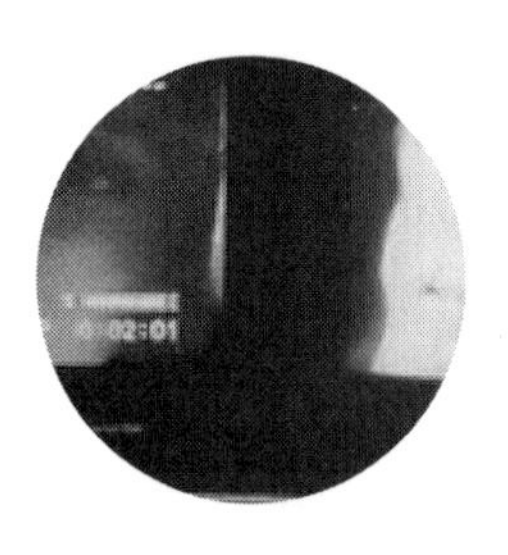

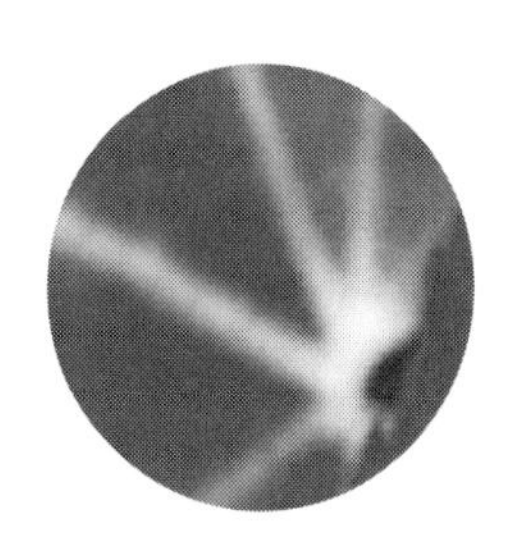

Acknowledgements

The editors and publisher gratefully acknowledge the teacher-reviewers listed below for their contribution to the development of this anthology.

Dan Blake
English Language Arts Consultant
Surrey School District
Surrey, British Columbia

Cathy Costello
Curriculum Consultant
The York Region Board of Education
Aurora, Ontario

Barbara Davison
Teacher, Charles P. Allen High School
Bedford, Nova Scotia

Jon Terpening
Teacher, Burnaby South Secondary School
Burnaby Board of Education
Burnaby, British Columbia

Jan Watson
English Department Head
Bayview Secondary School
The York Region Board of Education
Aurora, Ontario

To the Student

Welcome to the second edition of *Inside Stories I.* This anthology contains 28 stories, many of them recently written, and both Canadian and international in origin. Along with old favourites by familiar, established authors such as Ray Bradbury, Jane Rule, and Ernest Buckler, we have chosen stories from diverse far away countries such as Russia, China, Pakistan, Africa, and South America.

This collection is organized by common fiction elements in literature to give you a better understanding of what goes into the making of a good, effective story. We have added a new section entitled "Irony and Symbol" and have included "Stories for Further Reading" to give you a chance to explore fiction elements on your own.

Each unit starts with a brief commentary on a specific fiction element and introduces the stories in the unit. After each story, you will find response questions and activities to help you focus your study of that selection. At the back of the book (starting on page 246), there is a helpful glossary of fiction terms to review and use in your classroom story discussions and writings.

As the book title suggests, this line-up of stories invites you to "go inside" and explore memorable imaginative and real worlds that await you in these stories.

Happy reading.

G.K.
R.D.

UNIT ONE

The Story Experience

Ever since the first cave dwellers came back from the hunt and recounted the events to their companions, human beings have been fascinated by stories. Most people can remember times when somebody read a story to them or told them a story. As we grow older, we look for stories we will enjoy, mostly in the form of books, magazines, movies, video games, and television shows. Sometimes, though, we find stories in other places, such as a friend's phone call, a song, a letter, or an e-mail. What is the fascination with stories that keep us interested in continuing to read and hear them?

Do you remember a time when your imagination was totally caught up in a story you were reading or being told? It is when we have been taken into a fascinating different world from our own that we appreciate the appeal of stories as entertainment. We enjoy being taken into the lives and conflicts of others, into adventures beyond our personal experiences, and into new places and worlds totally different from the ones we know.

In addition to their value as entertainment, stories have a second appeal that interests readers. They tell us about the lives of the story's characters, allowing us to become familiar with a character's innermost thoughts and feelings. As that character responds to conflicts or needs, we, as readers, come to understand his or her motivation and understanding of life. This understanding can sometimes give us greater insight into ourselves, others in our lives, and our society.

The selections in this unit illustrate the range and depth of appeal that stories can have. The first story, "Barney," presents readers with an intelligent rat in a scientific experiment that gets out of control. The second story, "The Persian Carpet," gives us a glimpse into the actual truth of a remembered crisis. The third story, "The Friday Everything Changed," describes a conflict that leads to important insights into cultural traditions. Each selection offers a unique reading experience that will help you understand and appreciate the true value of stories.

The poison container was overturned and a trail of powder led to Barney's dish.

Will Stanton

Barney

AUGUST 30TH. We are alone on the island now, Barney and I. It was something of a jolt to have to sack Tayloe after all these years, but I had no alternative. The petty vandalisms I could have forgiven, but when he tried to poison Barney out of simple malice, he was standing in the way of scientific progress. That I cannot condone.

I can only believe the attempt was made while under the influence of alcohol, it was so clumsy. The poison container was overturned and a trail of powder led to Barney's dish. Tayloe's defence was of the flimsiest. He denied it. Who else then?

SEPTEMBER 2ND. I am taking a calmer view of the Tayloe affair. The monastic life here must have become too much for him. That, and the abandonment of his precious guinea pigs. He insisted to the last that they were better-suited than Barney to my experiments. They were more his speed, I'm afraid. He was an earnest and willing worker, but something of a clod, poor fellow.

At last I have complete freedom to carry on my work without the mute reproaches of Tayloe. I can only ascribe his violent antagonism toward Barney to jealousy. And now that he has gone, how much happier Barney appears to be! I have given him complete run of the place, and what sport it is to observe how his newly awakened intellectual curiosity carries him about. After only two weeks of glutamic acid treatments, he has become interested in my library, dragging the books from the shelves, and going over them page by page. I am certain he knows there is some knowledge to be gained from them had he but the key.

SEPTEMBER 8TH. For the past two days I have had to keep Barney confined and how he hates it. I am afraid that when my experiments are completed I shall have to do away with Barney. Ridiculous as it may sound there is still the possibility that he might be able to communicate his intelligence to others of his kind. However small the chance may be, the risk is too great to ignore. Fortunately there is, in the basement, a vault built with the idea of keeping vermin out, and it will serve equally well to keep Barney in.

SEPTEMBER 9TH. Apparently I have spoken too soon. This morning I let him out to frisk around a bit before commencing a new series of tests. After a quick survey of the room he returned to his cage, sprang up on the door handle, removed the key with his teeth, and before I could stop him, he was out the window. By the time I reached the yard I spied him on the coping of the well, and I arrived on the spot only in time to hear the key splash into the water below.

I own I am somewhat embarrassed. It is the only key. The door is locked. Some valuable papers are in separate compartments inside the vault. Fortunately, although the well is over forty feet deep, there are only a few feet of water in the bottom, so the retrieving of the key does not present an insurmountable obstacle. But I must admit Barney has won the first round.

SEPTEMBER 10TH. I have had a rather shaking experience, and once more in a minor clash with Barney I have come off second-best. In this instance I will admit he played the hero's role and may even have saved my life.

In order to facilitate my descent into the well I knotted a length of three-quarter-inch rope at one-foot intervals to make a rude ladder. I reached the bottom easily enough, but after only a few minutes of groping for the key, my flashlight gave out and I returned to the surface. A few feet from the top I heard excited squeaks from Barney, and upon obtaining ground level I observed that the rope was almost completely severed. Apparently it had chafed against the edge of the masonry and the little fellow perceiving my plight had been doing his utmost to warn me.

I have now replaced that section of rope and arranged some old sacking beneath it to prevent a recurrence of the accident. I have replenished the batteries in my flashlight and am now prepared for the final descent. These few moments I have taken off to give myself a breathing spell and to bring my journal up to date. Perhaps I should fix myself a sandwich as I may be down there longer than seems likely at the moment.

SEPTEMBER 11TH. Poor Barney is dead an soon I shell be the same. He was a wonderful ratt and life without him is knot worth livving. If anybody reeds this please do not disturb anything on the island but leeve it like it is as a shryn to Barney, espechilly the old well. Do not look for my body as I will caste myself into the see. You mite bring a couple of young ratts and leeve them as a living memorial to Barney. Females—no males. I sprayned my wrist is why this is written so bad. This is my laste will. Do what I say an don't come back or disturb anything after you bring the young ratts like I said. Just females.

Goodby

RESPONDING PERSONALLY

1. With a partner, review the events of the story as you understand them.
2. Name some famous novels and movies in which science experiments go wrong.

RESPONDING CRITICALLY

3. How did you respond to the surprise ending? What has happened? What was the foreshadowing of this plot twist?

4. Find three examples of irony in the last two paragraphs of the story.
5. On what grounds is Tayloe fired? How does the protagonist rationalize his dismissal?
6. What familiar conventions (patterns or rules) of the science fiction story and the fantasy story are found in "Barney"?

Responding Creatively

7. Write two or more diary entries for Barney.
8. Assume that Barney is recruiting female rats. Make a home page for him.

Problem-Solving/Decision-Making

9. For small group discussion: Do you think scientists should be free to perform experiments in secret?

As I stared down at the floor

I froze.

Hanan Shaykh
The Persian Carpet

When Maryam had finished plaiting my hair into two pigtails, she put her finger to her mouth and licked it, then passed it over my eyebrows, moaning: "Ah, what eyebrows you have—they're all over the place!" She turned quickly to my sister and said: "Go and see if your father's still praying." Before I knew it my sister had returned and was whispering "He's still at it," and she stretched out her hands and raised them skywards in imitation of him. I didn't laugh as usual, nor did Maryam; instead, she took up the scarf from the chair, put it over her hair and tied it hurriedly at the neck. Then, opening the wardrobe carefully, she took out her handbag, placed it under her arm and stretched out her hands to us. I grasped one and my sister the other. We understood that we should, like her, proceed on tiptoe, holding our breath as we made our way out through the open front door. As we went down the steps, we turned back towards the door, then towards the window. Reaching the last step, we began to run, only stopping when the lane had disappeared out of sight and we had crossed the road and Maryam had stopped a taxi.

Our behaviour was induced by fear, for today we would be seeing my mother for the first time since her separation by divorce from my father. He had sworn he would not let her see us, for, only hours after the divorce, the news had spread that she was going to marry a man she had been in love with before her family had forced her into marrying my father.

My heart was pounding. This was not from fear or from running but was due to anxiety and a feeling of embarrassment about the meeting that lay ahead. Though in control of myself and my shyness, I knew that I would be incapable—however much I tried—of showing my emotions, even to my mother; I would be unable to throw myself into her arms and smother her with kisses and clasp her head as my sister would do with such spontaneity. I had thought long and hard about this ever since Maryam had whispered in my ear—and in my sister's—that my mother had come from the south and that we were to visit her secretly the following day. I began to imagine that I would make myself act exactly as my sister did, that I would stand behind her and imitate her blindly. Yet I know myself: I have committed myself to myself by heart. However much I tried to force myself, however much I thought in advance about what I should and shouldn't do, once I was actually faced by the situation and was standing looking down at the floor, my forehead puckered into an even deeper frown, I would find I had forgotten what I had resolved to do. Even then, though, I would not give up hope but would implore my mouth to break into a smile: it would nonetheless be to no avail.

When the taxi came to a stop at the entrance to a house, where two lions stood on columns of red sandstone, I was filled with delight and immediately forgot my apprehension. I was overcome with happiness at the thought that my mother was living in a house where two lions stood at the entrance. I heard my sister intimate the roar of a lion and I turned to her in envy. I saw her stretching up her hands in an attempt to clutch the lions. I thought to myself: She's always uncomplicated and jolly, her gaiety never leaves her, even at the most critical moments—and here she was, not a bit worried about this meeting.

But when my mother opened the door and I saw her, I found myself unable to wait and rushed forward in front of my sister and threw myself into her arms. I had closed my eyes and all the joints of my body had grown numb after having been unable to be at rest for so long. I took in the unchanged smell of her hair, and I discovered for the first time how much I had missed her and wished that she would come back and live with us, despite the tender care shown to us by my father and Maryam. I couldn't rid my mind of that smile of hers when my father agreed to divorce her, after the religious sheikh had intervened following her threats to pour kerosene over her body and set fire to herself if my father wouldn't divorce her. All my senses were numbed by that smell of her, so well-preserved in my memory. I realized how much I had missed her, despite the fact that after she'd hurried off behind her brother to get into the car, having kissed us and started to cry, we had continued with the games we were playing in the lane outside our house. As night came, and for the first time in a long while we did not hear her squabbling with my father, peace and quiet descended upon the house—except that is for the weeping of Maryam, who was related to my father and had been living with us in the house ever since I was born.

Smiling, my mother moved me away from her so that she could hug and kiss my sister, and hug Maryam again, who had begun to cry. I heard my mother, who was in tears, say to her "Thank you," and she wiped her tears with her sleeve and looked me and my sister up and down, saying: "God keep them safe, how they've sprung up!" She put both arms round me, while my sister buried her head in my mother's waist, and we all began to laugh when we found that it was difficult for us to walk like that. Reaching the inner room, I was convinced her new husband was inside because my mother said, smiling: "Mahmoud loves you very much and he would like it if your father would give you to me so that you can live with us and become his children too." My sister laughed and answered: "Like that we'd have two fathers." I was still in a benumbed state, my hand placed over my mother's arm, proud of the way I was behaving, at having been able without any effort to be liberated from myself, from my shackled hands, from the prison of my shyness, as I recalled to mind the picture of my meeting with my mother, how I had spontaneously thrown myself at her, something I had thought wholly impossible, and my kissing her so hard I had closed my eyes.

Her husband was not there. As I stared down at the floor I froze. In confusion I looked at the Persian carpet spread on the floor, then gave my mother a long look. Not understanding the significance of my look, she turned and opened a cupboard from which she threw me an embroidered blouse, and moving across to a drawer in the dressing-table, she took out an ivory comb with red hearts painted on it and gave it to my sister. I stared down at the Persian carpet, trembling with burning rage. Again I looked at my mother and she interpreted my gaze as being one of tender longing, so she put her arms round me, saying: "You must come every other day; you must spend the whole of Friday at my place." I remained motionless, wishing that I could remove her arms from around me and sink my teeth into that white forearm. I wished that the moment of meeting could be undone and re-enacted, that she could again open the door and I could stand there—as I should have done—with my eyes staring down at the floor and my forehead in a frown.

The lines and colours of the Persian carpet were imprinted on my memory. I used to lie on it as I did my lessons; I'd be so close to it that I'd gaze at its pattern and find it looking like slices of red water-melon repeated over and over again. But when I sat down on the couch, I would see that each slice of melon had changed into a comb with thin teeth. The clusters of flowers surrounding its four sides were purple-coloured. At the beginning of summer my mother would put mothballs on it and on the other ordinary carpets and would roll them up and place them on top of the cupboard. The room would look stark and depressing until autumn came, when she would take them up to the roof and spread them out. She would gather up the mothballs, most of which had dissolved from the summer's heat and humidity, then, having brushed them with a small broom, she'd leave them there. In the evening she'd bring them down and lay them out where they belonged. I would be filled with happiness as their bright colours once again brought the room back to life. This particular carpet, though, had disappeared several months before my mother was divorced. It had been spread out on the roof in the sun and in the afternoon my mother had gone up to get it and hadn't found it. She had called my father and for the first time I had seen his face flushed with anger. When they came down from the roof, my mother was in a state of fury and bewilderment. She got in touch with the neighbours, all of whom swore they hadn't seen it.

Suddenly my mother exclaimed: "Ilya!" Everyone stood speechless: not a word from my father or from my sister or from our neighbours Umm Fouad and Abu Salman. I found myself crying out: "Ilya? Don't say such a thing, it's not possible."

Ilya was an almost blind man who used to go round the houses of the quarter repairing cane chairs. When it came to our turn, I would see him, on my arrival back from school, seated on the stone bench outside the house with piles of straw in front of him and his red hair glinting in the sunlight. He would deftly take up the strands of straw and, like fishes, they'd slip through the mesh. I would watch him as he coiled them round with great dexterity, then bring them out again until he had formed a circle of straw for the seat of the chair, just like the one that had been there before. Everything was so even and precise: it was as though his hands were a machine and I would be amazed at the speed and nimbleness of his fingers. Sitting as he did with his head lowered, it looked as though he were using his eyes. I once doubted that he could see more than vague shapes in front of him, so I squatted down and looked into his rosy-red face and was able to see his half-closed eyes behind his glasses. They had in them a white line that pricked at my heart and sent me hurrying off to the kitchen, where I found a bag of dates on the table, and I heaped some on a plate and gave them to Ilya.

I continued to stare at the carpet as the picture of Ilya, red of face and hair, appeared to me. I was made aware of his hand as he walked up the stairs on his own; of him sitting on his chair, of his bargaining over the price for his work, of how he ate and knew that he had finished everything on the plate, of his drinking from the pitcher, with the water flowing easily down his throat. Once at midday, having been taught by my father that before entering a Muslim house he should say "Allah" before knocking at the door and entering, as a warning to my mother in case she was unveiled, my mother rushed at him and asked him about the carpet. He made no reply, merely making a sort of sobbing noise. As he walked off, he almost bumped into the table and, for the first time, tripped. I went up to him and took him by the hand. He knew me by the touch of my hand, because he said to me in a half-whisper: "Never mind, child." Then he turned round to leave. As he bent over to put on his shoes, I thought I saw tears on his cheeks. My father didn't let him leave before saying to him: "Ilya, God will forgive you if you tell the truth." But Ilya walked off, steadying himself against the railings. He took an unusually long time as he felt his way down the stairs. Then he disappeared from sight and we never saw him again.

Responding Personally

1. What are the sisters doing at the opening of the story? What are they waiting for? What is your reaction to the dismissal of the old man? Compare your answers with a partner's.
2. Write a description of a place or a possession that was an important part of your childhood.

Responding Critically

3. What is the purpose of the flashback? Why does the author finish the story with Ilya's leaving in the past and not return to the present?
4. What is the truth about the Persian carpet theft? Who took it? Why? What effect is the lie likely to have on the protagonist?
5. Describe the protagonist's feelings toward her mother before and during the visit. How do they change?
6. With another student, brainstorm the conflicts in this story. Then write a paragraph based on your notes.

Responding Creatively

7. As the protagonist, write a letter to Ilya.
8. The daughter confronts her mother with the truth about the stolen carpet. Record their conversation in dialogue form.

Problem-Solving/Decision-Making

9. Describe a time when you or someone you know were lied to and then found out the truth. What did you do to resolve the problem?

And from that day on—for all the boys—the most important thing that happened at school, even more important than softball, was who would get to carry the water.

Anne Hart

The Friday Everything Changed

The last hour of school on Friday afternoons was for Junior Red Cross. The little kids would get out their Junior Red Cross pins and put them on and us big kids would start elbowing down the aisles to the book cupboard at the back to see who would get the interesting magazines. There was a big pile of them and they were of two kinds: the *National Geographic* and the *Junior Red Cross News*. Because the boys were stronger and sat near the back they usually got the *National Geographics* first, which meant they could spend the rest of Red Cross looking at African ladies wearing nothing on top, while us girls had to be satisfied with the *Junior Red Cross News*, which showed little African kids wearing lots of clothes and learning how to read. Apart from the magazines for the big kids and maybe the teacher reading a story to the little kids, about the only other thing that happened regularly during Red Cross was picking the two boys who would carry water the next week.

In our school the water bucket always stood on a shelf at the front of the room just behind the teacher's desk. First you'd make a paper cup out of a piece of scribbler paper, then you'd grab the teacher's attention from wherever it happened to be and then up you'd go to the front of the room for a drink from the water bucket.

It was kind of interesting to stand at the front of the room behind the teacher's desk and drink water. The school looked different from up there and sometimes you could get just a glimpse of an idea of what the teacher thought she was all about. I mean, from the front, looking down on those rows of kids with their heads bent over their desks and the sun coming in the windows and the blackboards and all that stuff on the walls, you might almost think, at first glance, that you were looking at one of those

real city schools—like in the health books—where the kids were all so neat and all the same size. But after the first strange moment it just became our school again, because you had to start adding in things like the coal stove and the scarred old double desks and the kids themselves. I mean, we just didn't look like the kids in those pictures. Maybe it was because we were so many different sizes—from the kids snuffling in the front rows over their Nan and Dan readers to the big boys hunched over their desks at the back—maybe it was because we wore so many heavy clothes all the time, or maybe it was because of something that wasn't even there at all but seemed to be on the faces of the kids in those city pictures: a look as if they liked being where they were.

But all that's a long way from Junior Red Cross and who would carry the water.

The water for our school came from a pump at the railway station, which was about a quarter of a mile away. One day long ago a health inspector had come around and had announced that water must be made available to the school. For a while there had been some talk of digging a well but in the end we got a big, shiny, galvanized water bucket and permission to use the railway station pump. And from that day on—for all the boys—the most important thing that happened at school, even more important than softball, was who would get to carry the water.

If you were a boy it was something you started dreaming about in Grade 1, even though there was not the remotest chance it could ever happen to you before at least Grade 5, and only then if the teacher thought you were big and strong enough. You dreamed about it partly because carrying the water meant you were one of the big guys, and carrying the water meant you could get away from school for maybe half an hour at a time. But mostly you dreamed about it because carrying the water was something real, and had absolutely nothing whatever to do with Nan and Dan and all that stuff.

So every Friday afternoon toward the end of Red Cross, when it got to be time for the teacher to pick the two boys who would go for water the next week, all the *National Geographics* came to rest like huge butterflies folding up their yellow wings and a big hush fell all over the back rows. And that's the way it had always been until one extraordinary afternoon when, right out of the blue, just after the teacher had picked Ernie Chapman and Garnet Dixon to carry the water, my seatmate, Alma Niles, put up her hand and said: "Why can't girls go for the water, too?"

If one of those German planes, like in the war movies, had suddenly appeared over the school and dropped a bomb, we all couldn't have been more surprised. A silence fell over the room and in that silence everyone looked at the teacher.

Now our teacher that year was named Miss Ralston and even though she came from River Hibbert we all liked her quite a lot. She was strict but she was never really mean like some of the teachers we'd had. Because she was young (she'd just finished Grade 11 the year before herself—River Hibbert had fancy things like Grade 11) she'd had quite a rough time the first week of school with the bigger boys. But she was pretty big herself and after she'd strapped most of them up at the front of the room before our very eyes (and even the little kids could see that it really hurt) things had settled down. The boys kind of admired Miss Ralston for strapping so hard, and us girls admired her because she was so pretty and wore nylon stockings and loafers all the time. But the really unusual thing about Miss Ralston was the way she sometimes stopped in the middle of a lesson and looked at us as if we were real people, instead of just a lot of kids who had to be pushed through to their next grades. And that was why, on that Friday afternoon when Alma Niles put up her hand and said: "Why can't girls go for the water, too?" we all turned and looked at Miss Ralston first instead of just bursting out laughing at Alma right away.

And Miss Ralston, instead of saying, "Whoever heard of girls going for the water?" or, "Are you trying to be saucy, Alma?" like any other teacher would, said nothing at all for a moment but just looked very hard at Alma, who had gone quite white with the shock of dropping such a bombshell. After a long moment, when she finally spoke, Miss Ralston, instead of saying, "Why that's out of the question, Alma," threw a bombshell of her own: "I'll think about that," she said—as if, you know, she *would*—"and I'll let you know next Friday."

The trouble started right away as soon as we got into the schoolyard, because all the boys knew, from the moment Miss Ralston had spoken, that something of theirs was being threatened and that, as long as there was the remotest chance that any girl might get to carry the water, they had to do everything in their power to stop it. Like driving a tractor or playing hockey for the Toronto Maple Leafs, carrying water was real, and because it was real it belonged to them.

So they went right for Alma as soon as she came out of school and that was when another funny thing happened. Instead of just standing back and watching Alma get beaten up, as we usually did when the boys were after someone, the girls rushed right in to try and help her. In the first place we all liked Alma, and in the second place we all had seen, as clearly as the boys, what our carrying the water might mean; that, incredibly, we, too, might get to skip school for half an hour at a time, that we, too, might get to sneak into Rowsell's store on the way back and, most dizzying thought of all, that we too might get to do something real.

And, because we were so intoxicated by the whole idea, and took the boys so much by surprise by standing up to them, we somehow managed to get Alma and ourselves out of the schoolyard with only a few bruises and torn stockings, leaving the boys in possession of the schoolyard where, as we could glimpse over our shoulders as we ran down the hill, they had begun to gather together in a single ominous knot.

And for the rest of that weekend, though of course we never talked about it in front of our parents, all we could think of, both boys and girls, was what was going to happen at school that coming week.

The first thing, clearly evident by recess on Monday morning, was that the boys had decided not to let us girls field at softball anymore.

Softball at our school used to go like this: every Monday morning at recess two of the bigger boys—that year it was usually Ernie Chapman and Junior LeBlanc—used to pick their teams for the week. Whoever came out on top in laddering hands up the softball bat got to pick first and the loser second and so it went—back and forth—until all the boys who were considered good enough to be on a team had been picked. Then Ernie and Junior laddered the bat again to see which side would get up first and the losing side took to the field to be joined by the little boys who hadn't been picked and us older girls who were allowed to act as sort of permanent supplementary fielders. And for the rest of the week the teams remained locked, at every recess and lunchtime, in one long softball game which had, as we discovered to our surprise several years later when the television came through, some strange rules.

The way we played, for example, every single boy had to get out before the other team could come in. And any boy hitting a home run not only had the right to bat straight away again but also to bring back into the game any boy who had got out. Which led to kids who couldn't remember their six-times table properly being able to announce—say, by noon on Thursday—"The score's now 46 to 39 because, in the last inning starting Tuesday lunchtime, Junior's team was all out except for Irving Snell, who hit three homers in a row off of Lorne Ripley, and brought in Ira and Jim and Elton who brought in the rest except for Austin who got out for the second time on Wednesday with a foul ball one of the girls caught behind third base ..."

Some days it got so exciting that at noon we couldn't wait to eat our lunches but would rush straight into the schoolyard, gobbling our sandwiches as we ran, toward that aching moment when the ball, snaking across the yellow grass or arching toward us from the marsh sky, might meet our open, eager hands.

So it was a hard blow, Monday morning recess, when Ernie Chapman whirled the bat around his head, slammed it down as hard as he could on home base and announced, "The first girl that goes out to field, *we break her neck*." We clustered forlornly around the girls' entry door knowing there was nothing we could really do.

"Oh Alma," mourned Minnie Halliday, biting the ends of her long, brown braids, "why couldn't you just have kept your mouth shut?" It was a bad moment. If we'd tried to go out to field they'd have picked us off one by one. We couldn't even play softball on our own. None of us owned a bat and ball.

If it hadn't been for Doris Pomeroy, we might have broken rank right there and then. Doris, who was in Grade 9 and had had a home permanent and sometimes wore nail polish and had even, it was rumored, gone swimming in the quarry all alone with Elton Lawrence, flicked a rock against the schoolhouse wall in the silence following Minnie's remark and steadied us all by saying: "Don't be foolish, Minnie. All we have to do is wait. They need us to field and, besides, they kind of like to have us out there looking at them when they get up to bat."

But it was a long, hard week. Besides not letting us field, the boys picked on us whenever they got the chance. I guess they figured that if they made things bad enough for us, sooner or later we'd go to Miss Ralston and ask her to forget the whole thing. But all their picking on and bullying did was to keep us together. Whenever one of us was tripped going down the aisle or got an ink ball in her hair or got trapped in the outhouse by a bunch of boys, it was as if it was happening to all of us. And looking back on that week—when there were so many bad feelings and so many new feelings in the air—it was kind of nice, too, because for the first time us girls found ourselves telling each other our troubles and even our thoughts without worrying about being laughed at. And that was something new at our school.

As for Alma, who kept getting notes thrown on her desk promising her everything from a bloody nose to having her pants pulled down, we stuck to her like burrs. But maybe Alma's hardest moment had nothing to do with bullying at all. It was when her cousin Arnold came over to see her Wednesday after school and asked her to drop the whole idea of girls going for the water.

"If they find out about it, Alma," said Arnold, "they'll probably take away the water bucket."

"Who's they?" asked Alma. She and Arnold had played a lot together when they were little kids and she was used to listening to his opinions on most things.

"Well, the health inspector," said Arnold, "and guys like that."

"They'll never take away that water bucket," said Alma, though she wasn't all that sure. "They don't care who carries the water as long as it gets carried."

"Alma," said Arnold earnestly, "the other guys would kill me if they ever found out I told you this but sometimes carrying the water isn't that much fun. On cold days it's real hard work. You're better off in the warm school."

Alma knew what it cost Arnold to tell her this but she stood firm. "I'm sorry, Arnold," she said, "but I'm used to cold weather. In winter I walk to school the same as you." So Arnold went away.

If Miss Ralston, as the week wore on, noticed anything unusual going on in her school, she gave little sign of it. She passed out the usual punishments for ink balls, she intercepted threatening notes and tore them up unread, she looked at Alma's white face, and all she asked about were the principal rivers of Europe. Nor were we surprised. Nothing in our experience had led us to believe the grown-ups had the slightest inkling—or interest—in what really went on with kids.

Only Doris Pomeroy thought differently. "Miss Ralston looks real mad," said Doris as we trailed in thankfully from Friday morning recess.

"Mad?" a couple of us asked.

"Yeah. Like when she comes out to ring the bell and we're all hanging around the entry door like a lot of scared chickens. She rings that old handbell as if she wished all those yelling boys' heads were under it. Of course, they do things differently in River Hibbert. I know for a fact that girls there get to play on softball teams just like the boys."

"On teams? Just like the boys?" But it was all too much for us to take in at that moment, so preoccupied were we with that afternoon's decision on the water. All that long, hard week it was as if Friday afternoon and Junior Red Cross would never come again. Now that it was almost upon us most of us forgot, in our excitement, at least for the time being, Doris' heady remark about softball.

So at lunchtime, just as the boys were winding up their week's game ("And real great, eh? Without the girls?" Ernie Chapman was gloating loudly from the pitcher's mound), when Miss Ralston, without her bell, leaped through our clustered huddles at the entry door and headed straight toward the softball field, she took us all completely by surprise. Crunch, crunch, crunch went Miss Ralston's bright red loafers against the cinders and the next thing we knew she'd grabbed the bat from Irving Snell and, squinting against the sun, was twirling and lining it before our astonished eyes.

"Come on! Come on!" cried Miss Ralston impatiently to Ernie who stood transfixed before her on the pitcher's mound. "Come on! Come on!" she cried again and she banged the bat against the ground.

"Come on! Come on!" cried Doris Pomeroy and we rushed after her across the cinders.

The first ball Ernie threw was pretty wobbly and Miss Ralston hit it at an angle so that it fell sideways, a foul ball, toward George Fowler's outstretched hand. "Ah-h-h-h-h," we moaned from the sidelines and some of us closed our eyes so we wouldn't have to look. But George jumped too eagerly for such an easy ball and it fell right through his fingers and rolled harmlessly along the ground.

Ernie took a lot more time over his second pitch. He was getting over the first shock of finding Miss Ralston opposite him at bat and by this time he was receiving shouts of encouragement from all over the field.

"Get her! Get her!" the boys yelled recklessly at Ernie and they all fanned out behind the bases.

Ernie took aim slowly. None of us had ever seen the pirouettings of professional pitchers but there was a certain awesome ceremony, nevertheless, as Ernie spat savagely on the ball, glared hard at Miss Ralston, slowly swung back his big right arm and, poised for one long moment, his whole body outstretched, threw the ball as hard as he could toward home base where Miss Ralston waited, her body rocking with the bat.

For a fleeting moment we had a glimpse of what life might be like in River Hibbert and then Miss Ralston hit the ball.

"Ah-h-h-h-h-h," we cried as it rose high in the air, borne by the marsh wind, and flew like a bird against the sun, across the road and out of sight, into the ox pasture on the other side.

"Ah-h-h-h-h-h ..."

We all stared at Miss Ralston. "School's in," she announced over her shoulder, walking away. Hitting the ball into the ox pasture happened maybe once a year.

That afternoon, toward the end of Red Cross, there was a big hush all over the room.

"Next week," said Miss Ralston, closing the school register, tidying her books, "next week Alma Niles and Joyce Shipley will go for the water."

She swept her hand over the top of her desk and tiny dust motes danced in the slanting sun.

Responding Personally

1. Recall an event when you became aware of the importance of dividing chores evenly and fairly without being influenced by gender.
2. Describe a memorable teacher who had a significant positive effect on you.

Responding Critically

3. Why are the boys so upset at the idea of the girls carrying the water bucket? What strategies do the boys use to pressure the girls to give in? How do the girls react?
4. What point does Miss Ralston make when she hits the home run? Why does no one protest when she announces that Alma and Joyce will go for water next week?
5. What qualities make this story entertaining? Does it have a significant message for readers? Explain.

6. In a small group, discuss the symbols of the water bucket and the baseball game. Then write a paragraph explaining the symbols and theme of this story.

Responding Creatively

7. With a partner, role-play a conversation between Miss Ralston and her school superintendent about her decision.
8. In pairs, make a crossword (with answers) using names, events, and objects from the story.

Problem-Solving/Decision-Making

9. For discussion: Describe a time when you had to make a difficult or controversial decision like Miss Ralston's.

UNIT TWO

Plot and Conflict

Most of our actions in life are determined by our needs, wants, and goals. Our concerns might be as basic as satisfying hunger or finding relief from pain; however, these needs may be as complicated as succeeding in a career or coming to a new understanding of ourselves. Whether basic or complicated, our needs, wants, and goals give us something to work toward, a motivation for our actions.

Story characters are similar to us. They, too, have needs, wants, and goals. Stories generally focus on a single concern of a character and usually follow the character's thoughts and actions as he or she seeks to fulfill that need, satisfy that want, or achieve that goal. As in life, the characters in stories cannot always get what they want without some struggle. Sometimes the characters are defeated by impossible obstacles. The forces that stand in the way of desired goals create conflict situations that the story characters must resolve before they can move toward the goal they have set for themselves. Usually, a story is over when an outcome or what results from the setting of the goal becomes clear to the character and reader. As in life, a character may succeed or fail, or there may be no clear outcome because the character's problem is not solvable.

An important benefit of reading stories is learning about problems other people face, the strategies they use to overcome problems and resolve conflicts, and their feelings about the experiences they have. When we measure their experiences against our own, we have the opportunity to understand and appreciate more about ourselves and others.

The stories in this unit describe three very different conflicts. The first, "Wild Horses," centres on the conflict a young boy feels about the treatment he receives from his older twin sisters. He wrestles with the fact that they treat him like a horse because horses are their great passion in life. The second story, "The Sea Devil," features person against nature as a man tries to free himself from a devil ray that is dragging him through the water. The final story, "The Carved Table," illustrates an internal conflict that the narrator has as she tries to find her own confidence and comfort with her new in-laws. These conflicts are like ones that we have in our lives. Conflicts in literature mirror the complex and fascinating struggles that are part of the experience of all human beings.

"You're a human child, aren't you? How boring."

Brian Fawcett
Wild Horses

My twin sisters were nearly seven years older than I was and they were the most normal sisters I ever knew. They hit me for no reason, and they kissed me for no reason, and they made me the victim of a hundred childish medical experiments. They also loved horses.

Now, all young girls seem to love horses, and there are at least a hundred theories about why. Most young girls love horses from books like *Black Beauty,* and some of the young girls in our town had a passionate but unrequited love for real horses they were too poor to own, and I'd heard that a few daughters of really wealthy people actually owned horses. My sisters weren't like any of those kinds of girls. They loved horses so much they created their own horses, rode them, made up stories about them, cured them when they were injured or sick, and generally made life miserable for them. But I had very little sympathy for those horses. They were dull and brutish animals, and for some reason I had never understood, my sisters thought I was one of them.

Because my sisters were twins, they presented a special problem for me: there were two of them, identical twins who shared the same mind, and they could surround me in a variety of thoroughly malevolent ways. The fact that they seemed to be able to surround nearly anyone didn't make any difference to me. When they surrounded and beat up my older brother's enemies, it didn't seem any different to me than when they surrounded and beat up my older brother, or surrounded me and did something to me I didn't like. There were too many of them and they were too agile for my liking. There was always one in front of me, whichever way I tried to escape. And the more I tried to escape, the more they thought of me as a horse they were trying to train.

They were small for their age, and were probably at least as aggressive as they seemed to me. My mother dressed them alike, and amused herself by correcting people who couldn't tell them apart, which nobody could. My sisters were content simply to know where the other one was, and where the horses were. They didn't much care about what which of them was which.

They decided I was one of their horses when I was about four years old, or at least that was when I became aware of it. In fact, they probably decided I was one of their horses when I was born, and no doubt, right from the beginning, treated me as their own tiny palomino colt. Since this made them good babysitters, my mother didn't object when they put me in a makeshift stall under the piano and tried to teach me to whinny. I may have whinnied before I spoke human language; I can't remember. My earliest memory is one of sitting underneath the piano stool being groomed by my sisters, and I had to recognize that I was *not* a horse before I could decide, in that formal recognition of the existence of the self we all experience, that I was a little boy.

Before I got to any of that, though, there were some other things I figured out. I wasn't the only horse in my sisters' stable. My older brother was just a year younger than the twins, and he fared much worse than I did. The twins considered him a bronco, and the two of them took turns trying to break him. Maybe they succeeded. My mother always told her friends how docile a child he was compared to the girls, and maybe that was why. I can remember the day he became a human being, too. They were herding him around the house on the end of a rope, pulling and pushing him from room to room, and he lost his temper. My sisters locked themselves in the bathroom and when my parents got home several hours later my brother was still trying to knock down the door to get at them. They found new ways to herd him around after that, and concentrated on training me.

I wasn't going to be able to do what my brother did for the foreseeable future, so I learned to whimper. My instinct was that a sick colt wasn't going to be much good to them, and if I was constantly on the limp they would at least spare me the endless trotting around the house that had driven my older brother to retaliate. It worked for a while, but I hadn't calculated my sisters' veterinary interests very well. They began to operate on me whenever I pulled up lame, and that was even less fun. I was tied up while they covered my legs and arms with bandages, and I had to stay in my stable until my mother came home, at which time they would tear off the bandages, stuff them back in the cupboard and tell me what awful things they would do to me if I squealed on them.

I suppose that if I were older, I might just have waited for them to grow bored with their sport. But I wasn't very old, and if I had tried to wait them out, I would have waited for a very long time, because my sisters had twice as much time as I had. I might still be under the piano stool. I couldn't fight back like my brother, nor could I appeal to him for help; he treated my plight with studied indifference. Maybe he thought it was better to leave well enough alone—horses that escape and go wild can be caught and tamed again.

My only hope was to outsmart them, but I wasn't old enough to outsmart the family dog, let alone twins who had me convinced they were everywhere at once. I began to hate horses, refusing to listen when my sisters generously tried to read *Black Beauty* to me. If I'd known what the word meant I would have known it was propaganda, but I didn't know anything except that I hated them all—white horses, black horses, Trigger, Silver, Champion; each and every horse in the world. They were too big and they had skinny legs, and every time there was a parade they pooped on the streets.

For a while I tried pretending I was a different animal when my sisters pretended I was a horse. I would meow and bark, cluck like a chicken, or moo like a cow. None of it worked. My sisters merely patted my snout and continued brushing my coat, or inspecting my fetlocks, or whatever they were up to. They outlasted everything I tried, even my heartbroken weeping. What saved me from them was the most natural of things in the equine universe—the presence of stallions.

My two horse-loving sisters, somewhere around the age of fourteen, discovered a magic place that was filled with beautiful stallions of every size, breed and colour. The place was the town they'd grown up in.

About the same time they discovered the stallions, the stallions discovered them. My sisters began to ignore me, and when they weren't ignoring me they were peering at me as if to say, "You're a human child, aren't you? How boring."

My sisters were never ones to do anything half-heartedly. They galloped into the hills where the stallions were waiting for them, and their long dark manes were intertwined with wild violets and the summer wind, and on the wind even I could hear the nervous whinnies of the stallions as my sisters rounded them up.

Horses are dull and stupid beasts, and these stallions were worse than the rest. They were in the back alley at night, behind the house, running through the hedges to brush their huge and hairy snouts against the windows where my sleepless sisters waited for them, waited to stroke their ears, their manes, their heaving flanks. Eventually my sisters went away with the stallions, leaving me with years and years to think about what they were, and what I was, and how, because of them, no one will ever ride me.

Responding Personally

1. With a partner, define *sibling rivalry*. Is it common? Explain.
2. In a group, offer ideas to explain the fascination of horses for some young girls.

Responding Critically

3. At first, how does the boy react to being treated as a horse? How does his behaviour change over the course of the story? Why?
4. For small group discussion: How are the sisters character foils to the boy? Are they unduly mean to him? Do they deserve his criticisms? How do they bring out his essential character? Report your ideas to the class.

5. Write a character sketch of the boy. Use adjectives to describe him and examples from the story to back up your points.
6. With a partner, discuss the symbolism of the horses. How does this symbol relate to the conflicts and characters involved?

Responding Creatively

7. Write a journal entry from the point of view of one of the sisters, describing how she feels about horses.
8. In pairs or triads, improvise a scene of typical conflict between siblings. Introduce the scene, and, afterward, comment on the scene's purpose and how the conflict might be resolved.

Problem-Solving/Decision-Making

9. Design a brochure about conflict management between siblings or family members. Identify topics that would be included.

Now at last he knew how the fish must feel when the line tightens and drags him toward the alien element that is his doom.

Arthur Gordon
The Sea Devil

The man came out of the house and stood quite still, listening. Behind him, the lights glowed in the cheerful room, the books were neat and orderly in their cases, the radio talked importantly to itself. In front of him, the bay stretched dark and silent, one of the countless lagoons that border the coast where Florida thrusts its great green thumb deep into the tropics.

It was late in September. The night was breathless; summer's dead hand still lay heavy on the land. The man moved forward six paces and stood on the sea wall. He dropped his cigarette and noted where the tiny spark hissed and went out. The tide was beginning to ebb.

Somewhere out in the blackness a mullet jumped and fell back with a sullen splash. Heavy with roe, they were jumping less often, now. They would not take a hook, but a practised eye could see the swirls they made in the glassy water. In the dark of the moon, a skilled man with a cast net might take half a dozen in an hour's work. And a big mullet makes a meal for a family.

The man turned abruptly and went into the garage, where his cast net hung. He was in his late twenties, wide-shouldered and strong. He did not have to fish for a living, or even for food. He was a man who worked with his head, not with his hands. But he liked to go casting alone at night.

He liked the loneliness and the labor of it. He liked the clean taste of salt when he gripped the edge of the net with his teeth as a cast netter must. He liked the arching flight of sixteen pounds of lead and linen against the starlight, and the weltering crash of the net into the unsuspecting water. He liked the harsh tug of the retrieving rope around his wrist, and the way the net came alive

when the cast was true, and the thud of captured fish on the floorboards of the skiff.

He liked all that because he found in it a reality that seemed to be missing from his twentieth-century job and from his daily life. He liked being the hunter, skilled and solitary and elemental. There was no conscious cruelty in the way he felt. It was the way things had been in the beginning.

The man lifted the net down carefully and lowered it into a bucket. He put a paddle beside the bucket. Then he went into the house. When he came out, he was wearing swimming trunks and a pair of old tennis shoes. Nothing else.

The skiff, flat-bottomed, was moored off the sea wall. He would not go far, he told himself. Just to the tumbledown dock half a mile away. Mullet had a way of feeding around old pilings after dark. If he moved quietly, he might pick up two or three in one cast close to the dock. And maybe a couple of others on the way down or back.

He shoved off and stood motionless for a moment, letting his eyes grow accustomed to the dark. Somewhere out in the channel a porpoise blew with a sound like steam escaping. The man smiled a little; porpoises were his friends. Once, fishing in the Gulf he had seen the charter-boat captain reach overside and gaff a baby porpoise through the sinewy part of the tail. He had hoisted it aboard, had dropped it into the bait well, where it thrashed around, puzzled and unhappy. And the mother had swum alongside the boat and under the boat and around the boat, nudging the stout planking with her back, slapping it with her tail, until the man felt sorry for her and made the captain let the baby porpoise go.

He took the net from the bucket, slipped the noose in the retrieving rope over his wrist, pulled the slipknot tight. It was an old net, but still serviceable; he had rewoven the rents made by underwater snags. He coiled the thirty-foot rope carefully, making sure there were no kinks. A tangled rope, he knew, would spoil any cast.

The basic design of the net had not changed in three thousand years. It was a mesh circle with a diameter of fourteen feet. It measured close to fifteen yards around the circumference and could, if thrown perfectly, blanket a hundred and fifty square feet of sea water. In the center of this radial trap was a small iron collar where the retrieving rope met the twenty-three separate drawstrings leading to the outer rim of the net. Along this rim, spaced an inch and a half apart, were the heavy lead sinkers.

The man raised the iron collar until it was a foot above his head. The net hung soft and pliant and deadly. He shook it gently, making sure that the drawstrings were not tangled, that the sinkers were hanging true. Then he eased it down and picked up the paddle.

The night was black as a witch's cat; the stars looked fuzzy and dim. Down to the southward, the lights of a causeway made a yellow necklace across the sky. To the man's left were the tangled roots of a mangrove swamp; to his right, the open waters of the bay. Most of it was fairly shallow, but there were channels eight feet deep. The man could not see the old dock, but he knew where it was. He pulled the paddle quietly through the water, and the phosphorescence glowed and died.

For five minutes he paddled. Then, twenty feet ahead of the skiff, a mullet jumped. A big fish, close to three pounds. For a moment it hung in the still air, gleaming dully. Then it vanished. But the ripples marked the spot, and where there was one there were often others.

The man stood up quickly. He picked up the coiled rope, and with the same hand grasped the net at a point four feet below the iron collar. He raised the skirt to his mouth, gripped it strongly with his teeth. He slid his free hand as far as it would go down the circumference of the net so that he had three points of contact with the mass of cordage and metal. He made sure his feet were planted solidly. Then he waited, feeling the tension that is older than the human race, the fierce exhilaration of the hunter at the moment of ambush, the atavistic desire to capture and kill and ultimately consume.

A mullet swirled, ahead and to the left. The man swung the heavy net back, twisting his body and bending his knees so as to get more upward thrust. He shot it forward, letting go simultaneously with rope hand and with teeth, holding a fraction of a second longer with the other hand so as to give the net the necessary spin, impart the centrifugal force that would make it flare into a circle. The skiff ducked sideways, but he kept his balance. The net fell with a splash.

The man waited for five seconds. Then he began to retrieve it, pulling in a series of sharp jerks so that the drawstrings would gather the net inward, like a giant fist closing on this segment of the teeming sea. He felt the net quiver, and knew it was not empty. He swung it, dripping, over the gunwale, saw the broad silver side of the mullet quivering, saw the gleam of a smaller fish. He looked closely to make sure no stingray was hidden in the mesh, then raised the iron collar and shook the net out. The mullet fell with a thud and flapped wildly. The other victim was an angelfish, beautifully marked, but too small to keep. The man picked it up gently and dropped it overboard. He coiled the rope, took up the paddle. He would cast no more until he came to the dock.

The skiff moved on. At last, ten feet apart, a pair of stakes rose up gauntly out of the night. Barnacle-encrusted, they once had marked the approach from the main channel. The man guided the skiff between them, then put the paddle down softly. He stood up, reached for the net, tightened the noose around his wrist. From here he could drift down upon the dock. He could see it now, a ruined skeleton in the starshine. Beyond it a mullet jumped and fell back with a flat, liquid sound. The man raised the edge of the net, put it between his teeth. He would not cast a single swirl, he decided; he would wait until he saw two or three close together. The skiff was barely moving. He felt his muscles tense themselves, awaiting the signal from the brain.

Behind him in the channel he heard the porpoise blow again, nearer now. He frowned in the darkness. If the porpoise chose to fish this area, the mullet would scatter and vanish. There was no time to lose.

A school of sardines surfaced suddenly, skittering along like drops of mercury. Something, perhaps the shadow of the skiff, had frightened them. The old dock loomed very close. A mullet broke water just too far away; then another, nearer. The man marked the spreading ripples and decided to wait no longer.

He swung back the net, heavier now that it was wet. He had to turn his head, but out of the corner of his eye he saw two swirls in the black water just off the starboard bow. They were about eight feet apart, and they had the sluggish oily look that marks the presence of something big just below the surface. His conscious mind had no time to function, but instinct told him that the net was wide enough to cover both swirls if he could alter the direction of his cast. He could not halt the swing, but he shifted his feet slightly and made the cast off balance. He saw the net shoot forward, flare into an oval, and drop just where he wanted it.

Then the sea exploded in his face. In a frenzy of spray, a great horned thing shot like a huge bat out of the water. The man saw the mesh of his net etched against the mottled blackness of its body and he knew, in the split second in which thought was still possible, that those twin swirls had been made not by two mullet, but by the wing tips of the giant ray of the Gulf Coast, *Manta birostris,* also known as clam cracker, devil ray, sea devil.

The man gave a hoarse cry. He tried to claw the slipknot off his wrist, but there was no time. The quarter-inch line snapped taut. He shot over the side of the skiff as if he had roped a runaway locomotive. He hit the water head first and seemed to bounce once. He plowed a blinding furrow for perhaps ten yards. Then the line went slack as the sea devil jumped again. It was not the full-grown manta of the deep Gulf, but it was close to nine feet from tip to tip and it weighed over a thousand pounds. Up into the air it went, pearl-colored underbelly gleaming as it twisted in a frantic effort to dislodge the clinging thing that had fallen upon it. Up into the starlight, a monstrous survival from the dawn of time.

The water was less than four feet deep. Sobbing and choking, the man struggled for a foothold on the slimy bottom. Sucking in great gulps of air, he fought to free himself from the rope. But the slipknot was jammed deep into his wrist; he might as well have tried to loosen a circle of steel.

The ray came down with a thunderous splash and drove forward again. The flexible net followed every movement, impeding it hardly at all. The man weighed a hundred and seventy-five pounds, and he was braced for the shock, and he had the desperate strength that comes from looking into the black eyes of death. It was useless. His arm straightened out with a jerk that seemed to dislocate his shoulder; his feet shot out from under him; his head went under again. Now at last he knew how the fish must feel when the line tightens and drags him toward the alien element that is his doom. Now he knew.

Desperately he dug the fingers of his free hand into the ooze, felt them dredge a futile channel through broken shells and the ribbon-like sea grasses. He tried to raise his head, but could not get it clear. Torrents of spray choked him as the ray plunged toward deep water.

His eyes were of no use to him in the foam-streaked blackness. He closed them tight, and at once an insane sequence of pictures flashed through his mind. He saw his wife sitting in their living room, reading, waiting calmly for his return. He saw the mullet he had just caught, gasping its life away on the floor boards of the skiff. He saw the cigarette he had flung from the sea wall touch the water and expire with a tiny hiss. He saw all these things and many others simultaneously in his mind as his body fought silently and tenaciously for its existence. His hand touched something hard and closed on it in a death grip, but it was only the sharp-edged helmet of a horseshoe crab, and after an instant he let it go.

He had been under the water perhaps fifteen seconds now, and something in his brain told him quite calmly that he could last another forty or fifty and then the red flashes behind his eyes would merge into darkness, and the water would pour into his lungs in one sharp painful shock, and he would be finished.

This thought spurred him to a desperate effort. He reached up and caught his pinioned wrist with his free hand. He doubled up his knees to create more drag. He thrashed his body madly, like a fighting fish, from side to side. This did not disturb the ray, but now one of the great wings tore through the mesh, and the net slipped lower over the fins projecting like horns from below the nightmare head, and the sea devil jumped again.

And once more the man was able to get his feet on the bottom and his head above water, and he saw ahead of him the pair of ancient stakes that marked the approach to the channel. He knew that if he was dragged much beyond those stakes he would be in eight feet of water, and the ray would go down to hug the bottom as rays always do, and then no power on earth could save him. So in the moment of respite that was granted him, he flung himself toward them. For a moment he thought his captor yielded a bit. Then the ray moved off again, but more slowly now, and for a few yards the man was able to keep his feet on the bottom. Twice he hurled himself back against the rope with all his strength, hoping that something would break. But nothing broke. The mesh of the net was ripped and torn, but the draw lines were strong, and the stout perimeter cord threaded through the sinkers was even stronger.

The man could feel nothing now in his trapped hand, it was numb; but the ray could feel the powerful lunges of the unknown thing that was trying to restrain it. It drove its great wings against the unyielding water and forged ahead, dragging the man and pushing a sullen wave in front of it.

The man had swung as far as he could toward the stakes. He plunged toward one and missed it by inches. His feet slipped and he went down on his knees. Then the ray swerved sharply and the second stake came right at him. He reached out with his free hand and caught it.

He caught it just above the surface, six or eight inches below the high-water mark. He felt the razor-sharp barnacles bite into his hand, collapse under the pressure, drive their tiny slime-covered shell splinters deep into his flesh. He felt the pain, and he welcomed it, and he made his fingers into an iron claw that would hold until the tendons were severed or the skin was shredded from the bone. The ray felt the pressure increase with a jerk that stopped it dead in the water. For a moment all was still as the tremendous forces came into equilibrium.

Then the net slipped again, and the perimeter cord came down over the sea devil's eyes, blinding it momentarily. The great ray settled to the bottom and braced its wings against the mud and hurled itself forward and upward.

The stake was only a four-by-four of creosoted pine, and it was old. Ten thousand tides had swirled around it. Worms had bored; parasites had clung. Under the crust of barnacles it still had some heart left, but not enough. The man's grip was five feet above the floor of the bay; the leverage was too great. The stake snapped off at its base.

The ray lunged forward, dragging the man and the useless timber. The man had his lungs full of air, but when the stake snapped he thought of expelling the air and inhaling the water so as to have it finished quickly. He thought of this, but he did not do it. And then, just at the channel's edge, the ray met the porpoise coming in.

The porpoise had fed well this night and was in no hurry, but it was a methodical creature and it intended to make a sweep around the old dock before the tide dropped too low. It had no quarrel with any ray, but it feared no fish in the sea, and when the great black shadow came rushing blindly and unavoidably, it rolled fast and struck once with its massive horizontal tail.

The blow descended on the ray's flat body with a sound like a pistol shot. It would have broken a buffalo's back, and even the sea devil was half stunned. It veered wildly and turned back toward shallow water. It passed within ten feet of the man, face down in the water. It slowed and almost stopped, wing tips moving faintly, gathering strength for another rush.

The man had heard the tremendous slap of the great mammal's tail and the snorting gasp as it plunged away. He felt the line go slack again, and he raised his dripping face, and he reached for the bottom with his feet. He found it, but now the water was up to his neck. He plucked at the noose once more with his lacerated hand, but there was no strength in his fingers. He felt the tension come back into the line as the ray began to move again, and for half a second he was tempted to throw himself backward and fight as he had been doing, pitting his strength against the vastly superior strength of the brute.

But the acceptance of imminent death had done something to his brain. It had driven out the fear, and with the fear had gone the panic. He could think now, and he knew with absolute certainty that if he was to make any use of this last chance that had been given him, it would have to be based on the one faculty that had carried man to his pre-eminence above all beasts, the faculty of reason. Only by using his brain could he possibly survive, and he called on his brain for a solution, and his brain responded. It offered him one.

He did not know whether his body still had the strength to carry out the brain's commands, but he began to swim, forward, toward the ray that was still moving hesitantly away from the channel. He swam forward, feeling the rope go slack as he gained on the creature.

Ahead of him he saw the one remaining stake, and he made himself swim faster until he was parallel with the ray and the rope trailed behind both of them in a deep U. He swam with a surge of desperate energy that came from nowhere so that he was slightly in the lead as they came to the stake. He passed on one side of it; the ray was on the other.

Then the man took one last deep breath, and he went down under the black water until he was sitting on the bottom of the bay. He put one foot over the line so that it passed under his bent knee. He drove both his heels into the mud, and he clutched the slimy grass with his bleeding hand, and he waited for the tension to come again.

The ray passed on the other side of the stake, moving faster now. The rope grew taut again, and it began to drag the man back toward the stake. He held his prisoned wrist close to the bottom, under his knee, and he prayed that the stake would not break. He felt the rope vibrate as the barnacles bit into it. He did not know whether the rope would crush the barnacles or whether the barnacles would cut the rope. All he knew was that in five seconds or less he would be dragged into the stake and cut to ribbons if he tried to hold on; or drowned if he didn't.

He felt himself sliding slowly, and then faster, and suddenly the ray made a great leap forward, and the rope burned around the base of the stake, and the man's foot hit it hard. He kicked himself backward with his remaining strength, and the rope parted and he was free.

He came slowly to the surface.

Thirty feet away the sea devil made one tremendous leap and disappeared into the darkness. The man raised his wrist and looked at the frayed length of rope dangling from it. Twenty inches, perhaps. He lifted his other hand and felt the hot blood start instantly, but he didn't care. He put his hand on the stake above the barnacles and held on to the good, rough, honest wood. He heard a strange noise, and realized that it was himself, sobbing.

High above, there was a droning sound, and looking up he saw the nightly plane from New Orleans inbound from Tampa. Calm and serene, it sailed, symbol of man's proud mastery over nature. Its lights winked red and green for a moment; then it was gone.

Slowly, painfully, the man began to move through the placid water. He came to the skiff at last and climbed into it. The mullet, still alive, slapped convulsively with its tail. The man reached down with his torn hand, picked up the mullet, let it go.

He began to work on the slip-knot doggedly with his teeth. His mind was almost a blank, but not quite. He knew one thing. He knew he would do no more casting alone at night. Not in the dark of the moon. No, not he.

Responding Personally

1. In your journal, write down your thoughts and feelings as you were reading this story.
2. Tell the class about an adventure you had in the wilderness.

Responding Critically

3. Quote the sentence that best embodies the story's moral. Then write a thematic statement for this story.
4. Decide what is the foreshadowing of danger in the story's opening section.
5. What is the climax of the story? What makes this moment the most suspenseful one and a turning point in the fortunes of the man?
6. In a paragraph, explain what the story reveals about the relationship between humans and nature.

Responding Creatively

7. With a partner, make a list of images from the story that you think would be dramatically effective in a video version of the story.
8. Draw a scene from the story. Add a caption and include a short write-up explaining why you chose this scene to illustrate.

Problem-Solving/Decision-Making

9. Outline the methods the narrator uses to solve his problem of being attacked by the ray. Explain what saved him.

Your capitalism, she wanted to say, is educating them in desperate ignorance.

Mary Peterson
The Carved Table

It was her second marriage and Karen sat at the round table in Marblehead with her new family, listening to their conversation and thinking of what her first husband would see, if he was there. He would notice, she thought, my new mother-in-law's enormous diamond, and he would see this new father-in-law's yachting jacket, and he would be disgusted. Might even say, "What are you doing here? You'll lose your soul to these people."

There were six around the table: she and her handsome husband, his parents, and her husband's spoiled-looking older brother and his glossy wife, who tossed her fine red hair and laughed at the right times and made little asides to the mother-in-law while the men held forth. Karen envied that sharing. She envied her thoroughbred sister-in-law who did not take it all so seriously. She herself took it too seriously and she couldn't shake off the feeling that something was terribly wrong.

She touched the carved wood edge of the table with one hand and with the other she reached toward her husband, rested her hand on his knee. He was always quiet during the cocktail hour, but also he listened with an odd, fixed smile: one of complicity—mesmerized like a twelve-year-old trying to learn the hard lessons of being an adult. When you were an adult you drank a lot; you kept up with your father in the drinking. This was difficult, since his father went to the bar for more bourbon often, and with each new drink he grew louder, and with each he had more to say and less that made sense. The man was well-educated, she reminded herself, and certainly he knew much about banking, airplanes, and stocks. But also, he believed children on welfare should be allowed to die, so that we could purify the society. He believed in capital punishment. He believed we should step up the arms race

and show more muscle abroad. Wars are different now, she wanted to say. We have nuclear weapons. We need a different set of rules. She did not say these things. Neither did she say that his capitalism created in the minds of the poor a need: they saw the television advertising, they saw the consumption of goods. How could they have any dreams but the ones he himself had? No wonder, she wanted to say, the Cadillac sits outside the tenement, and at the market people buy junk food with food stamps. What do they know about beans and meat? They know what they see on television, in the magazines; they know the Mercedes they see *him* driving. Your capitalism, she wanted to say, is educating them in desperate ignorance. Your free enterprise system.

She did not say any of it.

Her first husband would be thinking and maybe saying these things. He would know that the people around the table were the enemy, the very same she and he had fought when they lived in Chicago and worked against the war in Viet Nam. The same they had studied during the terrible sixties, the one they had hated.

"You're so quiet," her husband said, leaning toward her, giving her his hand. He was handsome and gentle and he didn't pontificate like his father and she loved him in spite of a score of things, and for a hundred others: not the least of them his stability, his good sense, his ability to be socially at ease with people, his open affection with her, the pure security of him.

"I was wondering," she said, "about the carving around this table." She tried to say it quietly, so the others wouldn't hear. "I know one of the wooden scallops was added, because one was broken, and I've been trying to guess if any of these—" and she ran her hand along the perimeter of the table "—is the new one. To see if it really fits so well."

"None have been added," he said. He seemed confused.

"You told me one was new. I remember."

"Karen's right," his father said. "One is new. I can't find it, either."

The other daughter-in-law and the mother had begun to play backgammon. They used an inlaid ebony board and when the dice were thrown they clicked like teeth. Her husband's brother had taken out an expensive cigar and was lighting it with great ceremony. He looked rich. His haircut looked rich and exactly right and his three-piece suit matched his shirt and tie exactly. He had a bored rich face and a sullen lower lip. You could not ask him a question because he would never answer it; he made light of everything.

The mother-in-law was beautiful and smooth-skinned and Karen had often watched her play with her grandchildren. She was the best of the family, but even in the best there was this other thing. In one game, the woman lined the children up to race. When they were ready, she broke away before she'd finished counting—she always won. "Your Grandmother lies," she told the children, laughing. One grandchild cried the first time she did it. The next time, the child who cried—a little girl—broke away early too.

Her first husband would have seen and understood all this, and although she didn't love him and didn't miss him, she respected his intelligence and he was more like her—shared with her a way of seeing. He would have observed her new husband's expensive suit, and her own diamond, and her own good haircut. But he's gone, she thought, and that's over. She released her new husband's hand. I'm seeing with my own eyes, she thought, and I mustn't blame it on anyone else. So now I must decide what to do.

Responding Personally

1. Which character do you identify with in the story? Why?
2. Do you feel Karen is having regrets about her new marriage? Share your ideas with a partner.

Responding Critically

3. With a classmate, make a chart of the different characters mentioned in the story. Analyze them according to appearance, comments or actions, and values. In a paragraph, compare and contrast Karen with the other characters.

4. What are some stream of consciousness sentences in the story that reveal Karen's inner conflict? Why does Karen not say aloud what she is thinking? With classmates, share your ideas on what you think is her internal conflict.
5. For small group discussion: The main symbols are the table and the wooden scallops. What do they represent? Are there other symbols? If so, identify them.
6. The story uses an indeterminate ending. Is it satisfying to the reader? Why or why not?

Responding Creatively

7. Write the e-mail message Karen might have sent her first husband after the story ends.
8. In groups of three, role-play a chance meeting at a restaurant or movie between Karen, her first husband, and her second husband.

Problem-Solving/Decision-Making

9. For discussion: If you were Karen at the end of the story, what would you do next? Make a prediction. Give reasons for your opinion.

UNIT THREE

Character

Our experiences in life lead us to meet and get to know many people, some of whom we call acquaintances and some of whom become good friends. Those we call good friends are usually people we have grown close to over a period of time. This observation about human relationships points out one of literature's chief values. Reading short stories that centre on the thoughts and actions of characters gives us easy access to personalities that we get to know better as we turn the story pages. Our involvement with the personality and problems of a character usually makes the story both interesting to think about and enjoyable. Because short stories focusing on character development provide us with opportunities to grow in our understanding of ourselves and others, these stories tend to be more meaningful and have more lasting impact than stories that do not develop their characters.

In life, the impressions we form of people we meet are based mostly on our sense of their appearance, what they say, what they do, and what others say about them. In reading, we learn about and judge characters in much the same way. Writers, however, usually give us even more information on which to base our impressions of a character. Writers can go beyond real-life experience by revealing to readers what a character is thinking and feeling. By providing information about a character's thoughts and feelings, the writer helps the reader know personally and immediately what is on the mind of a story's central character. Writers can also give readers a summary of what a character is like, thereby providing readers with a concise description to aid their understanding of a character more quickly than if they learned only about the character's physical description and actions, and others' responses to them.

The stories in this unit introduce readers to three rather unusual characters. "Alicia" lets us share the experiences of a young girl as she struggles to understand her older sister's mental illness. "The Father" gives us insight into a family and, in particular, the behaviour of the father. The third story, "The Old Woman," presents us with an elderly woman who is rapidly losing control over her life and needs to be in the care of her family or a nursing home.

When I tried to make her move, she abruptly gave me a malignant glance and began screaming "Judas! Judas!" at me.

Gabrielle Roy
Alicia

I must tell the story of Alicia; certainly it left the greatest mark upon my life; but how dearly it costs me!

Our Alicia with her huge dark blue eyes! And the so-strange contrast in her between those eyes and her coal-black hair! From Maman she had inherited also the loveliest eyebrows I remember ever to have seen, so roundly arched, so high and sharply delineated that they gave her glance an expression of amazement, of pain at the spectacle of life. She was still herself, with her pale, slender face; yet no, it was no longer Alicia. For already she no longer recognized those she so deeply loved; me alone, at times, she still knew. Her strange eyes would come back from so far away that to see them return filled me with dread; then she would look at me, smile at me as before; maybe she would even kiss me in the joy of rediscovering me; but she clung to me too tightly; and of her, of Alicia, I now was frightened! Then she would go back to where she had come from; her eyes would lose us all, relatives, friends, little sister. There would be no one but herself imprisoned within her queer look. Even then I could imagine how terrible it must be to be all alone within oneself.

"Whatever is the matter with Alicia?' I would go ask Maman.

At home we were always very reluctant to cry where anyone could see us. But how very often, at that time, when I went into the kitchen and found Maman alone, I caught her wiping her eyes with the corner of her apron! And she would hastily become a person with a great deal to do, who cannot be bothered. I would insist, "What's the matter with Alicia?"

They—I mean the grownups—were protecting me from the truth. They told me Alicia had nothing the matter with her. Is this what constitutes childhood: by means of lies, to be kept in a

world apart? But *they* could not prevent my seeking; and seeking by myself alone, without help, kept bringing me back into their world.

It was summer. A hotter, more brilliant summer I do not think there ever was on Rue Deschambault. We were as though readied for happiness, with our trees full of fruit, flowers all around the house, the lawn well-cropped. If I remember that summer so well, certainly it was because the season was so out of joint, so little in tune with our thoughts. Alicia alone seemed not to be aware of this contrast. She, who was the cause of our misery, withdrew from it as though she had no part in it; almost all the time she was humming.

One day she went up to the attic.

Constantly we would ask each other, worried, as though concerned about a tiny little child who had eluded our watchfulness, "Where is Alicia?"

And almost every day I would find the answer, "In the attic."

Once, though, it took me a long while to discover her. She had hidden herself in the depths of a dark cupboard, and when I at last found her, she was holding her head in her hands; this time she was crying.

Yet how was it that, having found her in an attitude which indicated she wanted to play hide-and-seek with me, I had no feeling that this was a game, nor any taste to join in it? In the past she and I had often played at hiding from each other; yet when we found each other once more, it was to bubble with laughter or accuse each other of cheating.

"Where is Alicia?" Maman would ask me.

And I would tell her; I would say: "Today she's braiding flowers and singing."

Why was it so sad to see Alicia spend hours weaving flowers together to make necklaces and bracelets for her adornment? Merely because she was no longer a little girl?...

One day in the attic Alicia put on a long white dress; around her waist she fastened a wide, sky-blue belt; in her hair she tucked some roses. I had never seen her look so lovely; and why was it sad to see her thus? She leaned out of the garret window toward the street and began scattering petals from the roses over the heads of the occasional passers-by. And she sang plaintively, "Here are flowers … good people.… Here are roses for you who walk by!…"

I don't know why, but I felt obliged to tell Maman that Alicia was throwing roses at the heads of the people in the street; one might have thought it somehow disgraced us.

"Go back up to her; try to distract her," said Maman. "Get her away from the window."

That day, however, Alicia did not even know me. When I tried to make her move, she abruptly gave me a malignant glance and began screaming "Judas! Judas!" at me. I was terribly afraid of Alicia, and ran off trembling. Yet it was only yesterday that Alicia had been taking care of me. She was responsible for me when Maman was very tired or when, wanting a full afternoon undisturbed to tackle some major sewing project, she handed me over to Alicia. She would say, "Alicia, don't you want to take the Little One for a walk? Will you look out for her?" Many an older sister would not have enjoyed constantly to be encumbered with a little girl like me. But Alicia never wounded me by seeming to be bored at the prospect of having to look after me.

It's true that I gave her the least possible trouble. We would leave the house together, and I was enchanted at seeing that we always took to the wilder side of the street. Never did we go—Alicia and I—toward town; that did not interest us; we would follow the narrow wooden sidewalk as far as the last house on our street. Then we would continue on across the fields, soon reaching our little grove of black oaks. In my childhood I thought this grove huge; I believed it a forest.… I have long realized that it was merely a largish clump of trees none too close together; it could not even wholly hide from us the distant gable of our house. No matter; it was among these small black oaks that I most fully felt the slightly dangerous mystery, the attractions, the solemn joy of being in the woods. Alicia helped me maintain this feeling. She would say to me, as we drew near our little oaks, "See! They look just like conspirators wrapped in their long, black coats." Then we forgot that the oaks were conspirators; we stretched out on the grass and watched the acorns fall, which sometimes landed right on our noses, when we had not been quick enough to dodge them. We could spend hours without exchanging a word. Already Alicia's thoughts, though, were not always happy. One day, having announced to her that when I grew up, I would do fine and beautiful things, Alicia told me sadly, "One says that, and then one never accomplishes anything except paltry things of no account."

"But mine will be great!"

Then, as though I were ill, exposed to I know not what, Alicia took me in her arms; she rocked me under a small oak tree rustling quietly in the wind, and I felt as though I were being cradled by the tree, the sky, by an inexhaustible tenderness. Yet when I pulled myself a little away from Alicia, I saw she was crying.

She told me: "You see, what I should like is that no one suffer. I'd like to spend my life preventing sorrow from touching people—Papa, Maman first of all, and then—oh, everyone. Why not everyone? How much hurt is in the world!"

Whereupon she had again clasped me in her arms, saying "I'll defend you. I won't let them do you harm!"

Now, however, she did not see how miserable we were. She remembered no one of us. She was our greatest unhappiness. When visitors came, we tried to hide her. There were some of our acquaintances and friends who still asked after her; the majority pretended they no longer included her in our number; yet some few still asked Maman, "And your daughter Alicia?"

Maman would explain how Alicia had been stricken with a fever which had, as it were, consumed her, adding that the doctors said of such illnesses: either they killed you or else the sequel was worse than death....

And I would go off into a corner of the garden to ponder her words. Whatever could be worse than death? I suppose I preferred to keep Alicia, unhappy, than to see her die. I was afraid lest now they wanted her dead. And from then on it was I who kept saying, "I'll defend Alicia. I won't let them do her any harm...." But one day she bit me savagely, and Maman noticed it.

She was trembling while she questioned me: "She hurt you? And—before this—has it ever happened that she hurt you?"

I could not wholly deny it; I was filled with bottomless terror.

Then it was that *they* decided to send Alicia away. *They* did not tell me the truth; *they* arranged the truth; *they* wholly transformed it. To all my desperate insistence—"Where is Alicia?"—*they* replied that she was in good hands, that perhaps she would return to health, that I must pray for her. And then, from time to time, I would still ask, "What's the matter with Alicia?"

And Maman, who had been so patient with me, put me off rather harshly. "Don't you see I'm so busy I don't know what I'm about? Leave me alone!" said Maman.

One day Papa and Maman were talking confidentially. I could tell by their faces when what they had to say was of interest to me. I pretended to be busy coloring my picture book. Papa and Maman glanced at me, then continued their conversation.

"It's a chance worth taking," Papa was saying. "Alicia loved her so!..."

"But she's only a child!... And to take her to such a place. Edouard!" said Maman. "Do you realize?..."

But Papa replied, "She was so fond of the baby! The joy of seeing her again, perhaps ... Shouldn't we try everything?"

"At her age," and Maman indicated me with a motion of her chin, "she could be marked for life...."

Papa insisted, "Remember how she loved her. If anyone can still do anything, it's surely our baby.... Only she can work that miracle...."

Then, realizing that they expected a miracle of me, I scuttled off and hid beneath the lower branches of the balsams. They hunted for me all afternoon; and when by evening they had not yet found me, they kept calling from the house, "Petite Misère! Christine!"

Underneath the evergreens in the darkness I was thinking of the picnics we so often had had together—just the two of us, Alicia and I. I presume that she had retained from childhood that need, that deep taste for independence, since we—we children—have so little true independence. In any case, to her as to me, nothing seemed less agreeable, more tiresome, than to sit down at the table for a meal. Thus quite often we persuaded Maman to give us permission to take some bread and jam, which we then consumed—was it not strange?—in a cornfield lying a little beyond the oak grove on the edge of the diminutive Seine River. This spot was not a bit comfortable; it afforded us no least level space on which to spread out our food, and obviously there was no view. Nonetheless, between the high rows of corn, Alicia and I had long taken delight in feeling as though we were closed in, well-protected, wholly hidden. We spent hours there, not in the least embarrassed by the fact that we had just enough room to sit down—to stoop, rather—between the close-planted stalks. The rustling of the big leaves, the occasional cry of a bird in the field, a sound as of rippling water which the wind made as it brushed the young ears, their silk, which we tore off to make ourselves beards or moustaches—to us all this was pleasure and high fun! Moreover—and this gave us a warm feeling of security—no one could possibly have come near us without our hearing them. In the cornfield we were as in a fortress, well-protected against others by the extreme pliancy of the stalks which, by the least change in the tone of their crackling, would have betrayed any invasions of our domain. Maman, however, eventually learned where we spent our afternoons; she had already begun to be anxious.

"In the corn! Why always go eat in the corn when there are such lovely other places?"

Very early in the morning Maman and I left to go there.

On the way I asked, "Have you locked Alicia up?"

Maman tried to laugh. "Locked up! What an idea! Of course not: she's in very good hands. She's being cared for by the best doctors."

But the small town we came to had a dismal look, unlike any other town. At least, so I saw it. Perhaps it was because of me. Since those days I have noticed that our thoughts have a great and curious power over things; on certain days they can make seem beautiful some wretched gray hovel; yet it can also happen that they make very ugly something that is not such in itself. This town seemed to me silent, bored, and somehow ill at ease in the sunlight. On a low hill a little outside the town, there towered a large, high building still more silent and more severe than all the rest; it was to this structure that we bent our steps. But I should mention that on arriving Maman had to ask directions, and she asked with a blush, in a low, unhappy tone. Now that we knew our way, we approached the high brick building and we soon became aware that it was placed in the midst of rather handsome grounds, with paths, seats, even swings, and many trees. But whence came the impression that despite these grounds, this structure had no means of exit anywhere? Maybe because of an iron fence all round it....

I remembered the field of corn; there one was locked in, true enough, but it was a very different thing!... Might not freedom reside in remaining within a very tiny space which you can leave if you have a mind to?

And how many trips had I already made with Maman, I thought to myself; some of them the finest in the world, in which I saw everything around me, others so sad they hid from me every vista. How strange is travel!

We knocked on a heavy door. A most impassive woman received us in a parlor. I say parlor for lack of a better word, since it was much better furnished than a convent or priest's house parlor. There was reading matter scattered about, good easy chairs gaily upholstered in chintz. Nevertheless, the idea would not have occurred to me to call this room a living room; you could be there only for the purpose of waiting ... waiting.... Such was the message of its silence; and yet all sorts of tiny sounds reached you from afar, like soft, almost fleeting footsteps, and the noise of keys: keys being turned in locks, keys swinging on a chain tied around the waist. Then I heard a peal of laughter, brief but frightening. I quickly held my hands to my ears. Maman seemed not to have heard it. She did not even notice how greatly I was terrified. Maman must have been deeply saddened no longer even to notice my own sadness. *They* say that sorrow brings people together. This is not always true; that day sorrow built a round wall tight closed about Maman as she sat erect on a straight-backed chair.

Then we heard footsteps coming toward us. The door opened. In the company of a blue-uniformed woman Alicia stood on the threshold. I say Alicia also for want of anything better. For it could not be Alicia who stood that way, her head bent, her body sagging as though broken, broken in I know not what abominable fashion!

And I wanted to cry out to the woman, to the building, to the whole red town, "What have you done to Alicia?"

The woman in uniform told Maman that *she* was much better, that obviously one could not expect too much, but that there was progress; then she left us.

Alicia, having sat down, remained motionless, unseeing.

"Alicia," said Maman, ever so gently, "don't you recognize me?" And Maman named herself: "Your mother ..." yet so embarrassed at having to say it that, like a wax taper, she seemed to burn and then melt away....

Alicia lifted her head a little; her eyes gave Maman a sideways glance; they swept over Maman's face as though it were that of a pleasant stranger ... and moved on elsewhere....

It's curious, but only then did I understand the words that, for some time now, Maman occasionally murmured to herself: "In my grave ... I wish I were in my grave!..."

Then she encouraged me with a brief gesture, not over-persuasive, as though she thought, "Do try—you—to work the miracle."

I slipped out of my chair. I moved close to Alicia. I put my arms around her waist, and I, also, called out to her, "Alicia!"

She smiled at me then, but it was like the smile of a small child, who recognized only very vaguely, by their faces, by their voices, those who love her. And my heart was broken; I know it must have been broken; I had no more courage left for the miracle. I let my head fall over Alicia's knees and I began to cry, suddenly remembering the rustle of the corn leaves above us.

Then I felt Alicia's hands, which softly stroked my wet cheek, as though to take stock of something inexplicable, very strange; and as though this hand was going forth to meet a habit long-forgotten and little by little rediscovered, it began to stroke my temples and my hair.

I turned my head on Alicia's knees. Her eyes were straining, focusing on a problem so absorbing that their pupils betrayed no slightest motion. You would have thought that a light from deep within her was striving to reach her eyes; and that made me think of long dark corridors through which one passes with a lamp in one's hand.... Had Alicia, then, so long a distance to traverse, alone in those black corridors? And was it recollection—that tiny glow which from time to time I saw shine behind her eyes?

Abruptly the light shone brighter there. With her small lamp shining in her hand, Alicia must have been nearing the end of the passage; thoughts, real thoughts, flitted across her face, but like veiled, uncertain passengers. Oh, how deeply stirring it is to behold a soul returning to a human countenance!

Alicia held me with her eyes. She looked at me intensely, smiled at me, found my name. She even spoke to me: "The Little One! It's you! Where on earth did you come from all by yourself?"

And then she cried out: "You've come to get me! It's you who have come to get me!... I knew you'd come!..."

And joy flooded her face as though it were the sun itself. Was it not a thing to marvel at? Returning to life, Alicia's soul first of all found joy! As though the soul had been made for joy!...

But at once her lips, her hands began to tremble! Why, immediately after joy, did despair cast itself upon her? Never before had I seen despair, and yet I recognized it. Such it surely was: a moment of lucidity, when you see your life and the harm you do others, all their unhappiness, yet no longer is it possible to change anything about it; it is too late; or else you were yourself only the instrument of suffering.... About that, one can do nothing.

This despair did not last long. Neither Maman nor I could have endured it longer ... nor Alicia herself. It was killing her, as it were, before our very eyes.

For one sole instant, then, we were ourselves within Alicia, and she herself was within us, and we were upon one single shore, close enough to touch, to see one another.... Then despair took Alicia away.... She began to draw off; and, abruptly, a darksome, invisible stream dug its way between us. Alicia, on the far shore, was moving away ... mysteriously ... she withdrew. I yearned to call her, so far gone was she already. And she, like someone about to disappear—she raised her hand and waved it toward us.

After this she seemed like a well-behaved little girl of about my age who toys with her fingers, crossing and then uncrossing them.

She died a few months later. *They* buried her, as one buries everybody, whether a person has died on the day of his death—or long before, because, maybe, of life itself.... What difference can there be here?... And why did they say of Alicia that God ... when He came to take her ... had shown her a mercy?...

Responding Personally

1. Describe a memorable childhood friend you once played with.
2. Record your views about why mental illness takes some people into other worlds.

Responding Critically

3. Who are the protagonist and focal character of the story? Compare ideas with a partner.
4. What foreshadowing is there of Alicia's increasing mental instability? Why couldn't her younger sister help her?
5. In a small group, discuss the meaning of the last paragraph. Do you think this paragraph provides an effective ending to the story? Why or why not?

6. Many readers prefer an entertaining story with a happy ending to a story such as "Alicia." What possible value is there in reading a sad story with an unhappy ending? Discuss.

Responding Creatively

7. Compose three diary entries for Christine about her changing relationship with Alicia.
8. With two classmates, improvise a conversation in which Christine and her parents finally talk openly about Alicia's illness. Perform the scene for the class.

Problem-Solving/Decision-Making

9. Write a speech about how people should treat and manage the situation of a family member who becomes mentally unstable.

"No," he said to himself. "No, it's your fault. It's always been your fault."

Hugh Garner
The Father

It wasn't the boy who gave him the invitation, but the boy's mother, his wife. Somehow even a little thing like this had become a shameful chore that the boy had avoided. Over the past year or two father and son had drifted apart, so that a strange shame and embarrassment colored every event that brought them into contact.

His wife had waited until the children had gone out after supper, the boy to play baseball and his older sister to run and scream with other teenagers in the schoolyard. Then she had said, "Johnny wonders if you'll go to the Boy Scout meeting with him tomorrow night?"

It was on the tip of his tongue to say, "Scout meeting! What do I look like?" Instead he asked, "Why, what's on there?"

"It's a father-and-son-banquet," she said.

"Why didn't Johnny ask me to go?"

"You know how he is—I guess he was too shy," she answered.

"Too shy! Too shy to ask his own father to go somewhere?"

"Well, I guess he was afraid you'd say no," she said.

"I'll think it over," he said grudgingly, knowing that he owed it to the boy, and also feeling that it might be a way of overcoming the barrier that had sprung up between them.

He didn't look forward to an evening spent in the company of a bunch of professional fathers, who were "real pals" to their sons. He had seen them making a nuisance of themselves, unable or unwilling to let their kids lead their own lives. They went swimming with their children, tried to umpire their ball games, and wrongly explained the displays at the museum and the animals at the zoo. He wouldn't normally mix with such men, but it was probably a big event for the boy, and it only happened once a year.

He poured himself a small drink and sat before the TV set, thinking of the coolness between him and his son and trying vainly to pinpoint its beginning. He knew that most of the time he was too preoccupied with other things to pay much heed to the boy's activities, but he had dismissed his misgivings with the thought, "He's only a twelve-year-old who wants to be left alone."

Over his drink he remembered the times he had been too harsh with the boy, and the times he had been curt and impatient. And with a feeling of angry revulsion he remembered siding with the teacher when he had been called to the school to discuss the boy's bad marks in reading. The principal had intimated that the boy's slowness might be caused by tensions in the home, but this he had vehemently denied. When the teacher had suggested keeping the boy in the same grade for a second year, he had acquiesced willingly, wanting only to get away from the place. The boy had looked up at him, bitten his lower lip, and had left the principal's office. From then on their distance one from the other was greater than ever.

On the evening of the banquet he was a little late getting home, having stopped in for a few drinks with a customer who was buying an industrial site. He ate warmed-over supper by himself, insisting all the while to his wife that there was no use eating when he was going to a banquet.

"You'd better eat," she said. "You've got to be at your best tonight."

"I'll be at my best, don't worry. I have a couple of drinks with a customer, and you're ready to shove me in an institution."

After he had bathed and shaved he put on his best suit. Though he had only contempt for scoutmasters, he was anxious to create a good impression for the sake of the boy. His suits were getting tight, as were the collars of his shirts. It was sitting at a desk all day did it, and not walking anywhere anymore. At the end of the war he had been lean and tough, but now he was middle-aged, fat, with his hair thinning fast on top.

He went downstairs and waited in the living room for the boy. The food his wife had pushed on to him had destroyed the glow from the pre-dinner drinks, so he poured himself a tall one for the road. From upstairs came the sound of his wife and son having their usual spat about the boy combing his hair. Though his wife and children quarrelled often, there was no tension between them at all.

The boy came down, wearing a pair of flannels and a blazer.

"Where's your scout uniform, Johnny?" he asked.

"We don't have to wear it if we don't want to," the boy said.

"I'll bet most of the other kids'll be wearing theirs."

The little boy shrugged.

His wife said, "Leave him alone, John. The reason he isn't wearing his uniform is that he only has half of it."

He couldn't remember how the boy had been dressed on Scout Night.

"Why hasn't he got the whole thing?" he asked his wife angrily. "We're not on the welfare, are we? Surely we could spend a few dollars for a complete scout uniform."

"Yes, but after you bought him the hockey pads and the rifle last Christmas he was afraid to ask you for anything else. He has the pants, belt and shirt, and all he needs is the neckerchief—"

"Afraid to ask me! That's all I hear around this place. What's the matter with this family anyway? God knows what the neighbors must think of me."

"There's no use getting angry," his wife said. "He'll have the whole uniform before long. He doesn't really need it tonight."

"Jimmy Agnew and Don Robertson aren't going to wear their uniform," the boy said, trying to mollify him.

He wondered angrily if the scoutmaster thought he was too cheap to buy the boy a uniform. Probably he said to his assistants, "It's too bad about little Johnny Purcell, isn't it? There's a kid been coming here for four months now and he still hasn't got a uniform." He felt a twinge of indigestion as he pictured the scoutmasters—a couple of big sissies running around in short pants playing woodsmen.

He said to his wife, "Listen, Helen, for God's sake take him downtown with you tomorrow and get the rest of the Boy Scout outfit. I don't want those goons down at the church thinking I'm too cheap to buy him one."

He expected the boy's face to light up at this, but he stood in the doorway wearing a blank expression. It was the same look the boy put on when he and his wife quarrelled, or when he had too much to drink and tried to talk to the kid man to man.

When they left the house, his daughter shouted after them, "Thank goodness we're getting rid of the men for the rest of the evening," and she and her mother laughed. The remark irritated him by pointing up the infrequency of such occasions.

As they walked down the street, he felt a warm pride as he stole glances down at the boy. Everyone said the youngster was the spit and image of himself when he was younger, and they both bore the same first name. Fatherhood was the rounding out of a life, probably what was meant in the Bible by a person having to be born again. But even as he thought these things, he knew it was only a fuzzy sentimentality brought on by what he had drunk.

The boy strode along beside him, his hands shoved deep into his pockets, even now managing to convey the distance that separated them. He wanted to get the boy into conversation, but could think of nothing to talk about that wouldn't sound wooden and contrived. He knew there must be a common plane of interest somewhere if he only knew what it was. The boy seemed content to walk along in silence, so he retreated into his own thoughts as they entered the business street that led to the church.

As they passed the schoolyard he asked the boy how the softball team was doing.

"All right. We beat the Tigers yesterday."

"What score?"

"Fifteen–eight."

"Say, that's great! Did you score any runs?"

"One, on Jimmy Agnew's two-bagger."

"Great! Did you put many guys out?"

"No."

He realized that he didn't even know what position his own son played, or even the name of the team. He thought it might be the Cardinals, but it might even be the Eskimos. He tried to picture the name on the front of the boy's sweater, but could not recall it.

"How many more games do you play?" he asked.

"Just two more in the regular schedule, one with the Eskimos tomorrow night, and one on Saturday with the Cardinals."

Well, the team wasn't the Tigers, Eskimos or Cardinals. He tried without success to think of the names of the other teams in the league. When they got home he'd have to take a peek at the name on the sweater.

They walked the rest of the way to the church in silence.

A young man in a clerical collar greeted them at the door to the parish hall, introducing himself as Mr. Redpath, the curate.

"My name's John Purcell," he said, smiling and shaking the curate's hand.

"How do you do. Though I know Johnny, and also Mrs. Purcell and your daughter Joanne, this is the first time I've had the pleasure of meeting you, I believe."

"Yes it is."

He was a little put out to discover that his family had a life separate from his. Of course they went to church fairly regularly, while he never went at all. When he was asked if he attended church he always answered, "Not since I was marched there with the army."

The young curate didn't seem to know what to do now that they had been introduced. He turned to the boy and asked, "How is the swimming coming along, Johnny?"

"Fine, Mr. Redpath."

The curate said, "He's going to be a great swimmer someday, is your son."

"Yes I know," he answered. Though he was aware that the boy had been going two nights a week to a neighborhood high school pool, he had never thought of him being an exceptional swimmer. He seemed to know less about the boy than anyone.

They were interrupted by the appearance of the scoutmaster, a very tall man with glasses, wearing a Boy Scout shirt and long khaki trousers.

Mr. Redpath said, "Mr. Purcell, I'd like you to meet Bob Wooley, the scoutmaster."

"How do you do," he said, putting out his hand. He noticed the two Second World War medal ribbons on the man's left breast, and knew the scoutmaster had never left the country.

The man peered at him as he took his hand. "I'm sorry, I didn't catch the name," he said.

"Purcell," he told him, his smile frozen on his lips.

"Oh yes, Johnny Purcell's father!"

He managed an amiable nod, but decided that the scoutmaster had come up to expectations.

"Well, Mr. Purcell, I have a disagreeable duty to perform," the man said, pulling a sheaf of tickets from the pocket of his shirt. Holding out two of them he said, "That will be three dollars please," giggling at the curate.

He decided to get into the spirit of the thing, and as he reached for his wallet he said, "Three dollars! Why I could have taken Johnny to a burlesque show for less than that."

The curate and the scoutmaster snickered politely, but he noticed them exchange significant glances. He handed over the money and pocketed the tickets.

"Right upstairs, Mr. Purcell," Redpath said, his tone much cooler than it had been.

When he looked around for the boy, he found that he had disappeared, and he climbed to the banquet hall alone.

It was a large room, probably used for the Sunday-school. It had an odor of sanctity about it, an almost forgotten smell of hymnbooks and varnish that carried him back to his choir-boy days. Down the middle of the floor stretched two long plank tables supported on sawhorses, and covered with paper tablecloths. There were about fifty places set. Hanging on the walls were various exhibits of scoutcraft, and in one corner of the floor a tent and an imitation campfire had been set up, surrounded by imitation grass probably borrowed from the church cemetery next door.

He spied his son, in the company of two other boys and their fathers, looking at some photographs on the wall, and walked over to them. As soon as he reached his side, Johnny led him away from the others and began pointing out the various knots that were illustrated by twisted pieces of sashcord mounted on a board.

"Have you anything on exhibition, Johnny?" he asked the boy.

"Only the Cree mask I made last winter."

Cree mask! He'd never seen the boy making a mask, though he had wondered vaguely what he was doing in the basement sometimes. "Let's go over and see it," he said, and the boy led him around the tables to the opposite wall.

They stopped before a wooden mask, painted red and yellow with holes cut in it for the eyes and mouth. He was no judge of such things, but he was amazed at the workmanship and artistry of it. He could see the tremendous amount of work that had gone into its carving, and felt an immeasurable loss as he realized he had not even inquired what the boy was doing all those long evenings in the basement.

"Say, Johnny, that's great! It's just great!" he said, slapping his son on the shoulder. "I never knew you could make things like that. Did you carve it out of a single piece of wood?"

"No. I had to glue two pieces together."

"Where did you get it—the wood I mean?"

"Mr. Robertson gave me it. He helped me shape it, but I did most of the carving."

"Who's Mr. Robertson?"

"Don's dad. *You* know Don Robertson." "Oh sure." He didn't know one boy or girl who came to the house from another. It must be the tall blond kid who went to the movies with Johnny on Saturday afternoons.

Two boys and their fathers came along and stood beside them, admiring the mask. He was about to tell them it was the work of his boy, but Johnny was suddenly in a hurry to get away. "Come on, Dad," he said quickly. "There's a picture over here of Danny Mahaffey winning his mountaineer badge."

He followed the boy to the end of the room, aware for the first time that his son was ashamed of him. As he pretended to look at the photograph, he wondered what he had ever done to make the boy feel that way. Now he remembered the times he had met Johnny with his friends on the street, and had received only a grudging wave of the hand from him. And he remembered going to watch the boy play ball in the schoolyard, and being pointedly ignored throughout the game.

The dinner consisted of the usual creamed chicken and peas, and the after-dinner speeches contained the usual intramural jokes shared by the scoutmaster, the curate and the boys. During the meal he became quite friendly with the father sitting on his right, not realizing until it was too late that he had acted overloquacious, his earlier drinks, plus the heat of the hall, making him talk and laugh too loudly. Once he stopped himself in time before criticizing the scoutmaster's home-service ribbons.

Johnny hardly spoke to him at all, but attached himself conversationally to a boy sitting on the other side of him. They laughed at the speakers' jokes and whispered conspiratorially, ignoring him completely.

From the anecdotes of the speakers, he was surprised to find that many of the fathers had visited the summer camp, and that some even joined in the weekend hikes. He had been under the impression that only the scoutmaster and his assistant went along with the boys. He began to feel like an outsider, and he glanced along the line of adult faces across the table, wondering if he was alone in his feelings. Every other father had the look of belonging.

Just when the curate's stories were beginning to gripe him, that young man ended his speech and announced a five-minute break before the presentations would be made. With a loud clattering of chairs, the boys and their fathers pushed themselves away from the tables.

When he looked around for Johnny he saw him running towards the stairway in company with the boy who had been sitting beside him. He pushed his way through the crowd to the back door of the hall, and stood on the outside steps and lit a cigarette.

The door behind him opened and man came out.

"It's kind of stuffy in there," the man said.

"Yes, in more ways than one."

The man laughed. "You said it. This is the first time I ever came to one of these things."

"Me too."

"Good. I was afraid I was the only one."

"My name's Purcell—John Purcell," he said, offering the other his hand.

"Glad to know you, John. I'm Charley Murdoch—Murdoch's Radio and Appliances up on Lorimer Street."

"Sure, I've seen your place."

"What line of business are you in?"

"I'm with Saunders, Gordon and Company, real estate and industrial appraisers."

"Fine."

Murdoch lit a cigarette and they stood talking about the Boy Scouts and their unfamiliarity with dinners such as this one. They discovered they had a couple of mutual friends downtown.

Then Murdoch said, "This may not be the exact place for it, but I've got a bottle of liquor in the car. Would you care for a snort before we go back to hear how the curate got marooned on the island in Elk Lake, or how the scoutmaster's tent blew down in the storm last summer?"

"You're a lifesaver," he said.

They walked to Murdoch's car, which was parked against the cemetery wall. Murdoch took a pint of whiskey from the glove compartment, and then began to feel around in the back seat. "I've got a small bottle of ginger ale back here somewhere," he said. "Yeah, here she is!" He straightened up and took the top off the ginger ale with a practised motion beneath the dashboard.

They had three good drinks apiece before Murdoch said, "Maybe we'd better go back inside. If we don't get in there soon that kid of mine will tell his mother for sure."

The presentations were well under way by the time they returned to the hall, and there was a craning of necks by almost everyone as they crossed the floor. As each boy's name was called, he and his father would go forward to the dais, where the scoutmaster presented the badges to the father, who then presented them to his son.

Johnny gave him an apprehensive look when he sat down, and then crowded as far away from him as he could get, trying to associate himself with the boy and his father on the other side of him.

He sat back in his chair and gave his attention to what was taking place on the platform, smiling to himself as the boys and their fathers left the tables, received their presentations, and returned to their seats. As the whiskey began to work, he took a friendly view of the affair, and applauded heartily as each twosome sat down. He mentioned to his neighbor that it looked like an investiture at Buckingham Palace, but the man shushed him with a finger placed to his lips. Once, he tried to catch Murdoch's eyes, but his new friend was looking somewhere else.

When the assistant scoutmaster called out, "John Purcell," he tapped his son on the shoulder and stood up, saying, "That's both of us." There were a few titters from the boys, and a couple of the fathers smiled. Johnny hurried to the platform without waiting for him. He followed, grinning at the upturned faces he passed. Now that he was on his feet the room began to blur, and the faces at the tables seemed to run together into one big bemused grin. He grinned back, feeling a fellowship with every other father in the room. They really weren't a bad bunch once you got to know them.

As he climbed the steps to the dais the scoutmasters stared at him with a quizzical look, and the curate turned to the audience with an embarrassed smile. The scoutmaster approached him and said, "Mr. Purcell, I am happy and honored to present this lifesaving certificate to your son, John Purcell, and also this badge for hobbycraft. It is not very often that a boy as young as John earns a lifesaving certificate, and I'm sure you must be very proud of him."

He nodded his head and murmured his thanks. When he looked down to face the boy, the room swam before his eyes, but he managed to stay erect. "Here you are, Johnny," he said, handing the boy the certificate and badge. He felt prouder than he had ever felt in his life before, and just handing the awards to his son like this didn't seem enough to mark the moment. In a paroxysm of pride and happiness he grasped the boy's hand, and facing the audience, held it aloft like a referee signifying the winner of a boxing bout.

There was a short burst of embarrassed laughter from the tables. He turned to the scoutmaster, who was trying to smile with little success. The boy broke away from him and ran back to his chair, his chin lowered on his chest.

He stepped down carefully from the dais, and, with all the dignity at his command, made his way to his table. As he turned around its end, he staggered slightly and fell against it, pushing the planks askew from the sawhorse that supported them. Two or three of the fathers prevented the whole thing from toppling, but a vase of flowers and a couple of plates fell to the floor with a loud crash.

After apologizing profusely to those who were picking up the flowers from the floor, he reached his chair with extra-careful steps and sat down. Some of the small boys stared at him wonderingly, but their fathers showed an absorbing interest in what was going on upon the platform. He now saw the humor of the accident, and turned to wink at his son to show that everything had turned out all right after all. The boy was sobbing silently, his thin shoulders shuddering beneath his blazer.

Suddenly he was shamed by the enormity of his act, and had to prevent himself from taking his son on his knee and comforting him as he had done when the boy was younger. He pulled himself together instead, setting his mouth in a defiant line, and stared unseeing at the people on the platform.

When the meeting came to an end, he was the first person out of the hall. He walked about fifty yards down the street and stood in the shadows of the cemetery wall. The boy hurried down the steps and came running towards him, and, when he drew abreast, he stepped out and took him by the arm.

"I'm sorry, Johnny," he said, placing his arm around the small boy's shoulders. "I acted a little silly in there, but it was really nothing. It'll be forgotten in a day or two."

The boy turned his tear-stained face up to him and said, "Leave me alone, Daddy, please."

"Look, Johnny, I'm sorry. I didn't mean to hurt you like that. Listen, I'll tell you what we'll do—we'll go downtown tomorrow and I'll buy you a whole new Boy Scout outfit."

"I'm not going to the Scouts any more."

"Sure you are. Listen, you've got that lifesaving certificate and—"

"I left them behind. I don't want them anymore."

"But, Johnny, listen—"

"Leave me alone, Daddy, please!" the boy cried, breaking away from him and running down the street.

"Johnny! Wait for me. Johnny! Listen, I want—"

The boy was half a block away by now, running as fast as he could. He hurried after him, knowing it was useless but afraid to let him go like this. Why had he done it, he asked himself, but could get no answer from either his head or his heart. Had there always been something between himself and the boy that neither of them understood? "No," he said to himself. "No, it's your fault. It's always been your fault."

Already the running form of the boy was two blocks ahead of him, and he would soon be out of sight entirely. As he hurried after him he wondered if he would ever be able to draw close to his son again.

Responding Personally

1. What feelings about fathers are evoked by this story?
2. With a partner, describe a time when you had a "falling-out" with a parent.

Responding Critically

3. What is the betrayal in the story? What causes it? How responsible is the father for the betrayal? What errors does he make?
4. Why does the son run away from his father? Will he ever forgive his father? Give reasons for your opinion.
5. What epiphany does the father have at the end of the story? Is he likely to change? Exchange your ideas in a small group.
6. The exposition and antecedent action of this story provide insights into the source of conflict between father and son. What attitudes and events lead to their drifting apart? Is the father accurate in thinking that "he seemed to know less about the boy than anyone"? Explain.

Responding Creatively

7. With a partner, role-play a conversation between two other fathers at the banquet after the Purcells leave.
8. Write a note that the father leaves for his son to read the next morning.

Problem-Solving/Decision-Making

9. For small group discussion: Do you feel that the father and his son will ever be reconciled? Give your opinion using evidence from the story. If the father had a second chance to relive the evening, would he do anything differently? Explain.

"She can't go wandering about the building not knowing where she lives."

Elizabeth Brewster
The Old Woman

1

The old woman knew she was getting a new neighbor in the apartment across the hall from her. The apartment had been vacant for nearly two weeks. There had been a painter; she had peered in curiously and seen him sloshing a creamy white paint on the walls. There had been someone in to check the refrigerator and the stove. Then, this morning, the movers had come, a truck from out of town, and had brought up table, chairs, buffet, chesterfield, bed, a whole array of cardboard cartons filled with—what? dishes? The new tenant had come, too, in a taxi with suitcases, and had gone out again for a long time, leaving the movers to put in the furniture by themselves. She was a woman of perhaps thirty-five or forty, the old woman decided, not a young girl. But no husband in evidence, so far as she could tell.

In the evening, when the old woman came out of her own apartment to put some garbage down the garbage chute, she could tell that the tenant had come in again because there was a bright light in the hall of the apartment shining visibly under the front door. Having got rid of the garbage, the old woman came back and stood in front of her neighbor's door. She would knock and give her a welcome, she decided.

The new tenant came to the door of the apartment, wearing an apron over her slacks. She was tall, thin, almost hollow-cheeked, with straight hair and brown eyes. She looked questioningly at the old woman. The floor of the small kitchen and of the dining area was crowded with boxes, some still full, some now empty, and masses of wrapping paper lay scattered about. Some dishes, some books, the old woman could see. "I just thought I'd say

'Yoo-hoo,'" the old woman said. "I'm Mrs. Cornish, your neighbor from across the hall. I saw the movers come with your things."

"Thank you, Mrs. Cornish," the woman said (not telling her own name, though). "I'd ask you in, but you can see what a mess the place is."

"Oh, well, another time. I used to be quite friendly with the boys who were here before."

"Boys? I thought the caretaker had said there was one man, an old bachelor."

"One? Oh, no, there were two of them—two boys. Well, I'll be off and leave you to your unpacking. Don't tire yourself."

Back in her own apartment, Mrs. Cornish stood in the kitchen looking around with perplexity. Had she done the errand she set out to do? Oh, yes, of course, she had emptied the garbage. That woman looked too thin—needed fattening up. Had there been only one tenant before? Maybe the boys had been earlier. Could that be? She did sometimes lose track of time.

She made her way, rather painfully because of her stiff right knee, into her living room, where she settled herself in her big leather armchair in front of the television. But she couldn't keep her mind on those TV antics. She picked up the newspaper, tried to read it. Too many obituaries, too many of them of people younger than herself. The cooking section was more cheerful. That's what she should do. Bake a batch of something—cookies? biscuits?—and take it across to the new tenant.

2

By the time the second knock came, Florrie Middleton was beginning to feel that she just might possibly manage to get the kitchen in order for breakfast tomorrow morning. The books could wait until tomorrow; as a matter of fact, it would be ages before they were really in order; but at least she could get them up off the floor and into bookcases. Now who could this be?

Another neighbor? People sometimes said that highrises were unfriendly places, but this one didn't seem to be.

After all, it was the same old dear as before, Mrs. Cornish was it? A stocky, shapeless figure in a cotton house-dress, her feet thrust into slippers. Wisps of white hair were straggling out of her bun, forming an aureole effect around her pink face. This time she was carrying a mounded plate covered with a napkin.

"Sugar cookies," she said, beaming at Florrie and holding out the plate. "I knew you wouldn't have time to bake when you're unpacking."

"That's very kind of you. I'd better put these on another plate so you can have yours back."

"Oh, no, no," Mrs. Cornish cried, backing away. "Keep it until you've eaten the cookies. Then you can bring it back to me. That's my door right over there—see?"

Florrie didn't really like cookies, but it was good of the old dear to bring them. Breaking off a corner of one, she nibbled at it. Poor old biddy—she must've forgotten the salt. Thank goodness she didn't need to eat them before the old woman's eyes. She felt half guilty sneaking the cookies into the garbage later, and she had to guess a time that might seem reasonable for them to be eaten so that she could return the plate to Mrs. Cornish.

The old woman's apartment was full to bursting with furniture, much too much of it. Probably she hadn't been able to bear the thought of giving up the second china cabinet with all its little figurines, the extra coffee tables, the oak table which was just too big for the dining nook, the Victorian love seat crowded up next to the chesterfield. Florrie found her way past footstools and hassocks to a chair (for of course the old woman would not allow her to leave without a cup of tea and a piece of her lemon bread, just freshly made).

"I know your name now," the old woman said, "from the card on your door. F.J. Middleton. Is it Miss or Mrs?"

"Florrie Middleton. I'm not married. But call me Florrie, if you like."

"Flossy, did you say?"

"No, Florrie." (She hadn't noticed before that the old woman was hard of hearing; but perhaps it was because she was across the room from her now instead of standing right beside her.)

"Florrie's a pretty name. Mine's Blanche, but nobody's called me that for years. Where do you work, Florrie?"

"At the university."

"The university … University Hospital, you mean?"

"No. I'm in the Arts Building. I teach."

"You teach art?"

"No, I teach Canadian history."

"Oh, so you're a teacher. I wanted to teach when I was a girl. I wanted to teach so bad. But my mother wouldn't let me. She made me take a dressmaking course instead."

"And did that work out? Did you enjoy dressmaking?"

"Oh, well enough. But that wasn't the way I earned a living when I had to. I kept a boardinghouse. For years. And do you know where I kept a boardinghouse?"

"Some other town? Here in Saskatoon?"

"Right here where we're standing. My boardinghouse was where this building is now."

"Oh. Then you must've made some money when this building was built."

"Well, yes, you could say so. But I was sorry to see my house torn down. Oh, my goodness, I was sorry. All those years and all those people."

"That must've been quite an experience, eh? Lots of people coming and going. Did you have a family too?"

"Two sons. Perce, my second son, works for the Post Office. If you're ever around at noon, you may see him coming and going in the hall. He has his lunch with me three days a week. Perce and his wife brought up his family in that house of mine; but when it was sold my daughter-in-law wanted their own house separate." (There was resentment in her voice. A sore point, Florrie conjectured.)

"You have grandchildren, then?" Florrie asked politely. Older people always like to talk about their grandchildren.

"Oh, yes. Three boys and a girl. One of the boys is going to university too. In Regina. He's very clever. He's so clever I can't understand a word he says sometimes."

She was still talking happily about the grandchildren some time later when Florrie decided she must leave.

"Oh, no, Mrs. Cornish, not another cup of tea. I must get back to my marking. Must hand back their essays tomorrow, you know."

"Oh, you teachers. You always work so hard. Won't you take some of the lemon bread with you? Or some of this nut bread?"

"No, no—really, Mrs. Cornish, you mustn't stuff me. Save it for your son's lunch. I must be off."

A sweet old soul, she thought, back at her own dining table, over which the essays were scattered. A sweet old soul, but almost too chatty.

3

The old woman was restless. The tall apartment building seemed to her almost creepily quiet. The builders had boasted, justifiably, of the soundproofing between apartments, so that, even if her hearing had been good, she could not have heard her neighbors unless they had given the loudest and noisiest of parties. And they were all so quiet. Most of them were widows, like herself, or retired people. No life left in them. She used to knock at Mrs. Baron's door farther down the hall, hoping for a little gab, but lately Mrs. Baron didn't answer the door. She must either be sleeping or too deaf to hear her. And of course that school teacher—Flossy, had she said her name was?—was out all day. But now she was in. The old woman could see the light shining under the door.

When she knocked at the door, Flossy—no, Florrie it was—came to answer, the tap still turned on at the kitchen sink. "Oh, Mrs. Cornish," she said, "I thought you were the paper boy. I'm just getting myself some dinner."

"Why don't you come and have a bite with me? I've got enough for two," Mrs. Cornish said eagerly.

"Oh, I couldn't. I've already put things on. I'm afraid I don't have enough for two, but why don't you come and have some coffee with me—say nine or nine thirty?"

The old woman was back at eight. "I forgot what time you said," she told Florrie.

"Oh well, never mind. I'll put the coffee on to perk, and you can have some ice cream with me while we wait for it to be ready."

She pushed aside a pile of books at the end of the dining table, dished up the ice cream in heavy cereal bowls, with fruit poured over it.

"How are you finding the children?" the old woman asked.

"The children?"

"The children you teach. You did say you were a teacher?"

"Oh, they're not children—at least they don't think they are. I'm at the university. Remember?"

Mrs. Cornish fumbled with the brooch—her mother's amethyst brooch—which fastened her collar. It was something she did when she was embarrassed. She was always forgetting things, or not hearing things clearly. Was this woman a student? Come to think of it, she looked younger than she had thought at first, with her hair falling around her face. She peered at Florrie with her dim old eyes; then her gaze wandered to a painting on the wall above the dining table. It was an odd painting, rather sad, with dark, diminished human figures clinging together on a park bench under brown trees. "Did you paint that?" she asked Florrie.

"Oh, no, I'm no artist. My uncle's a painter. He did that. Do you like it?"

"Very much," Mrs. Cornish lied, "but isn't it just a little—gloomy?"

"Oh, Uncle George's work is gloomy. He got his start as a war-time painter with the Canadian Armed Services. He painted all those great, dark canvasses, with khaki uniforms and gray skies and mud. All brown and gray, with a hint of blood-red now and then. He's never got away from his war-time style in peace-time subjects. At least he uses the same colors."

"But he came back from the War. He wasn't killed, like Matt, my son."

"You had a son killed?"

The coffee was ready, and Florrie poured it into two big brown mugs. The old woman found her mug heavy to hold. She had broken her wrist two years ago when she fell on the ice, and it was still weak.

Matt's face, with his naval cap at a jaunty angle, as in his last photograph, hovered just in front of Mrs. Cornish's eyes, cut off her vision. "It was a submarine got him," she said. "Those Germans."

"I hardly remember the War," Florrie said, almost apologetically. "I was just a small child then. It must've been terrible for you."

"I'll never forget the day I found out," Mrs. Cornish went on. "Never. I'll never get over it. You know, I've never been to church since."

"You found you couldn't believe?" Flossy—Florrie?—asked. "Because God allowed your son's death?"

Mrs. Cornish considered this. What had belief to do with it? "It was because he always went to church. He was such a good boy. I couldn't go to church without being reminded of him. Ida—my daughter-in-law—keeps trying to get me to go. She says it would be consoling. But I'll never go. Never."

For a moment she had almost thought Florrie was Ida, and she must argue with her.

"Still, you have your other son," Florrie said. "Your have your grandchildren."

So she was supposed to be lucky, the old woman thought. Count her blessings.

"Tell me about the days when you ran the boardinghouse," Florrie said. "Are some of the people who boarded with you still around?"

So she wanted to change the subject, did she? Take her mind off Matt? Perhaps just as well.

"Most of them are dead or moved," Mrs. Cornish said. "Some of them are too high up now to want to remember when they lived in a boardinghouse. Some of them are old, too. But some of them come back. Only last year a couple came back ..."

What were their names? They had become engaged at her place, those two. She frowned, laboriously trying to remember. Then faces, incidents, began to come back. She talked on, began to realize that she had been here at Florrie's a long time, saw Florrie stealing a glance at her wrist watch. Mustn't wear out her welcome. She lumbered to her feet, and Florrie rose to help her.

"Don't mark the children's papers too hard," she told Florrie.

4

Florrie was full of anxiety about this job, which she felt she must do well on. She had been late getting her doctorate, and full-time permanent academic jobs were becoming scarce. She was lucky to be here, and she must make a good impression, earn tenure and promotion. She was conscientious about her teaching and although she didn't think of herself as drivingly ambitious, she was ambitious enough. She didn't have too much time for distractions, especially distractions she didn't enjoy. When the old woman took to knocking on her door every evening, she became just such a distraction.

"You were late coming in tonight," the old woman said one evening.

"How do you know?" Florrie asked. "Do you watch when I come in?"

"I walked past several times earlier, and your lights weren't on. Now they're on. I could see the light shining under the door."

So that was it.

Late the next afternoon, Florrie came in quietly, did not turn on the light in the hall, but reached around the corner to turn on the kitchen light. That, she was more or less certain, did not show outside in the hall.

That evening, she heard the old woman limping several times along the hall. Once she halted in front of Florrie's door, but she did not knock. Florrie held her breath, pen poised over paper.

Then she heard the old woman's slow, halting walk along the passageway towards her own door. Florrie felt guilty, as though she had hidden from her grandmother. But she couldn't, she just couldn't, chat with the old dear, sweet as she was, for hours every evening. If she would come just once a week, say Sunday afternoon—or every other Sunday afternoon—

But then, Sunday was the day Perce and Ida came and took the old woman out to Sunday dinner. Florrie knew, because she had met them once in the hall, on the way out. She had been wrapped up in her dressing gown, on the way to put some clothes in the washer; she would have liked to ignore them, and be ignored, but the old woman had stopped her, had insisted on introducing her, though as usual she couldn't remember Florrie's name. Perce was a mild little man, Ida the dominant one in that family, Florrie conjectured.

Florrie almost never turned her light on in the hall now. After all, she told herself, she might as well save power. It was some time before she talked again to the old woman; but one Saturday afternoon in late November, coming in with a load of groceries, she found herself sharing the elevator with her. "Oh, it's Flossy—Flossy Milton, isn't it?" the old woman beamed. "What have you been doing with yourself?"

"Oh, I've been here. Busy."

"You've been on the night shift at the hospital, haven't you? I never see your light any longer."

Florrie felt guilty immediately, and invited the old woman to come in to tea. Thank goodness she had bought cake at the bakery; otherwise the poor old soul would probably have wanted to cook something for her. She looked at Mrs. Cornish, perched rather forlornly on the chesterfield in the living room. Was it her imagination, or had the old woman gone downhill, even in these few months?

One evening, when Florrie was sitting up late marking December examinations, her doorbell—the one down on the main floor—

rang. Who could be ringing her doorbell at midnight? Was it a prank or an emergency? She crossed the room, pressed a button, and spoke into the intercom. "Yes. Who is it?"

"It's me," a woman's voice said, rather loudly.

"Who's me? I think you must have the wrong place. I wasn't expecting anybody."

She went back to her work, but the bell rang again immediately.

"Who's this?" she asked in exasperated tones.

The voice was desperate. "Me, Me, Me. Let me in."

"Can't you tell your name? I can't let in someone I don't know."

"It's—It's—Cornish. I've locked myself out of my apartment and I can't get the caretaker."

"Oh—well, of course, come on up." She pressed the button that opened the front door, stepped out in the hall to see the old woman when she got off the elevator.

"You must say your name, Mrs. Cornish," she said. "Voices sound different over the intercom, you know."

"I forgot it for a minute," the old woman said, woebegone. "The caretaker usually lets me in. He must be out."

"Maybe he was in bed," Florrie said. "It's getting late. Where were you? At your son's?"

"No, I was just out walking."

By herself? At midnight? Oh dear. The poor woman.

Florrie telephoned the caretaker. His doorbell, he said, hadn't rung, but he'd come and let Mrs. Cornish in. She usually left her keys on the kitchen table, he said.

Florrie met the son in the hall by chance a few days later. "You must have quite a problem sometimes with Mother," he said, shaking his head. "I can imagine."

Florrie smiled uncomfortably. "Of course, she's a dear ..." she said. Ought she, she wondered, to suggest that Perce and Ida take Mrs. Cornish home to live with them? But they saw her regularly; they must know how she was. Probably Ida wouldn't have her, in any case.

The morning she took the taxi to the airport to fly to Winnipeg for the Christmas holiday, she stopped on the way to the elevator to prop a parcel up against Mrs. Cornish's door. Gift of guilt, she thought, half smiling. Chocolates to make up for her neglect. But if she had thought she would get away without a few words with the old woman, she was mistaken. Florrie had reached the elevator and was pressing the button when Mrs. Cornish's door opened suddenly and she peered out. She picked up the parcel, waved at Florrie, and came hobbling towards her. "Somebody must've left a parcel at my door by mistake," she said.

"It's yours," Florrie said, repeating the words twice because the old woman couldn't hear. "Your name's on it. It's a parcel from me."

"Isn't she a darling?" the old woman said to the caretaker's wife, who was passing through the hall. "She's given me a present."

The elevator came. "Can't stay—taxi's waiting—Merry Christmas!" Florrie called back, shutting her eyes as the elevator plunged with her down to ground level. Ah, how good to have a little time away from students, faculty, committee meetings—and from Mrs. Cornish!

5

Sometimes when the old woman awoke in the morning she was not the old woman or Mrs. Cornish. She was Blanche, little Blanche Tissington on her way to school with her lunch in a red lard-kettle; or young Blanche Tissington going to a dance all dolled up in her best. Oh, she was a lively one, that Blanche Tissington, with her dimples and her curls and her twinkling eyes and feet. Flossy Milton (or whatever her name was) would never guess. And it was hard, if you had been little Blanche Tissington when you woke up in the morning, to find yourself imprisoned in old Mrs. Cornish's body, which was so heavy and stiff. What a to-do it was just to take a bath, to let yourself down gradually, your knee-joints creaking, into the tub; and then to hoist yourself up and out when the bath was over. And it was either that or take a shower, which was even more dangerous. Remember the old man in the boardinghouse who had slipped, who had broken his hip, who had nearly drowned.

It was hard, now, to keep times and seasons separate. She had to look out the window to see if the snow was still on the ground or if the trees were coming out into new leaves. In the morning, she was not sure of the time because she had forgotten to wind the kitchen clock and it had stopped. Her watch never had been reliable. The radio told her the time of day, and the newspaper told her the date, but she forgot what they told her from one hour to the next.

It was lilac season when she met that Flossy person in the hall, and she—Flossy? Florrie?—said, "Why don't you come to dinner tonight?"

"Oh, you're always so busy," the old woman said.

"Not tonight. It's vacation. I'm going away soon for the summer."

So she went to Florrie's for dinner; and Florrie had roasted a chicken and cooked a pie. She wouldn't have thought Florrie was so domestic.

"Somebody knocked at my door asking for a relative of yours," the old woman said. "At least, he asked for Dr. Middleton. I told him there was a nurse named Middleton here, but no doctor that I knew of."

"I'm Dr. Middleton," Florrie said.

"You are! You never told me you were a doctor. I thought you were a nurse."

"I'm not a nurse. It's just my doctorate of Philosophy. Who was he? The man who asked for me?"

The old woman didn't understand all that, but she tried to remember the man. "He didn't tell me his name," she said. "He was tall. I think he was fair—or was he dark? He had a moustache, I think."

"Are you sure it wasn't a beard?"

Florrie was laughing at her. Oh—wait until she was old, really old. Then she would know.

In the fall—it must have been fall, because the leaves were changing color—one day when she was on her way out of the apartment building, she saw Florrie in the lobby with a man. The same man? He had a moustache, not a beard. He reminded her in some distant way, she realized, of Edward Cornish, her husband, who had gone away such a long time ago. But she never mentioned Edward Cornish, never. It was only her son she missed. Matt. Put the thought of Edward out of her mind. He was not to be remembered. Even after all these years. She scuttled past Florrie and the man and out the door without speaking. Now why did she do that? What would Florrie think? She clutched her brooch and sighed.

Not long afterwards, Florrie moved out of her apartment, although not out of the building. "I'm just moving up to the sixteenth floor, Mrs. Cornish," she told the old woman. "I'll still be a neighbor."

"But I'll never remember where it is," the old woman said. Then, "Why do you want to move?"

"I need more space. For a study. This apartment is really very small, you know."

The old woman looked around the living room. "It's as big as mine," she said forlornly. But of course if she wanted to go—

One day when she had started to walk home from shopping, the old woman stopped to rest on a bench in front of the Public Library. She was just closing her eyes for a little snooze when she heard a voice. "Why, Mrs. Cornish," the voice said, "what are you doing here? Are you all right?"

It was Florrie.

"I'm just resting," the old woman said. "I was wondering if I'd make it the rest of the way home."

"Would you like to take my arm? I can help you."

So the old woman got up, and allowed Florrie to lead her. She hoped she was not delaying her too much; she had to take such tiny steps.

"Would you like to see my new apartment?" Florrie asked when they arrived in the lobby. "Come up and I'll make you some tea and toast."

So she went up; and really it was a much bigger, more elaborate apartment altogether. But there was Florrie's dining table with the books on it, and there was her funny, gloomy painting by the man who had been in the War. (Oh, Matt, Matt, where are you?)

"You see I have a really fine view across the river," Florrie said. "I sit here at breakfast and watch the traffic on the bridge."

Yes. That was more cheerful than the painting.

But there was someone at the door. It was that man, the man with the moustache, though he no longer had the moustache. Or was it a different man? He didn't look like Edward Cornish after all. It must have been the way the light had fallen on him.

"Oh, Reg," Florrie said. She sounded as though she were used to him. Then, "Mrs. Cornish, I think you met Reg once in the hall, didn't you?"

"You're the lady who thought Florrie was a nurse," he said, smiling at the old woman. "Lucky you never tested her with a sprained ankle."

"We're having toast and honey, Reg," Florrie said. "Do you want some too?"

"There's nothing I'd like more than toast and honey. Almost nothing."

He was a pleasant man, and she could see he was prepared to be kind to old ladies. But it was not the same. No, it was not the same. She did not stay long.

But she had to go back. She had to go back and knock at Florrie's door again, because she couldn't find her own apartment. She had walked across the hall to it, and it wasn't there. Somebody else lived there.

She was almost crying when Florrie opened the door. "It's gone," she said. "My apartment's gone."

"Your apartment's gone?" Florrie said, staring at her. "It can't be."

Mrs. Cornish pointed across the hall. "Somebody named Jones lives there now. They must just have moved in."

"Oh!" Florrie exclaimed, as though something suddenly made sense. "You live on the fifth floor, Mrs. Cornish, don't you remember?"

"But isn't this the fifth floor?"

"No. The sixteenth. Just a minute and I'll come downstairs with you. Reg, I'll be right back, darling."

Oh, now she knew what she had done. She had been so foolish. Florrie and that man—Herbert, Reg—would laugh and laugh at her when they were alone together. She tugged at her brooch, clutched her handbag, felt herself go scarlet. Yes, she had her key. And here they were on the fifth floor, and at her door. Someone else, a young couple, lived in Florrie's apartment. She had never got acquainted with them.

6

Florrie dabbed at her eyes with a handkerchief. She wasn't sure whether she was sad or hysterically amused. Both, perhaps. "But what am I to do about her, Reg? She can't go wandering about the building not knowing where she lives."

"Do? But she has a son, doesn't she? You said she had a son. Isn't it up to him? Why should you do anything?"

"Well, I'll call him. I'll tell him about this. I wonder if he's home from the Post Office. I'd hate to get that awful wife of his."

Florrie detested telephoning. It was one of her little phobias. She would almost rather drop into the Post Office and look Perce up. But Perce mightn't like to be looked up. She picked up the phone book.

"I thought there wouldn't be many Cornishes," she said, "but there's a P. Cornish, a P.A. Cornish, a P.E. Cornish, an R.P. Cornish. I suppose Mrs. B. Cornish is our Mrs. Cornish."

"It sounds confusing. Why don't you write a letter to Mr. Percy Cornish at the Post Office?"

"I'm not sure if he's Percy or Perceival. Well, yes, I think I'll write a letter, after all. It's easier that way. But ought I to? They'll put her in a nursing home, that's what they'll do. Would I want that done to me?"

"She isn't you, you know, Florrie."

"Isn't she? I'm not sure about that." She sighed.

But she would write the letter, just the same.

Florrie saw the old woman only one more time; sitting, as she had before, on a park bench, but this time in front of the cenotaph, with the last of the leaves falling around her. She was wearing a hat with a large brim, and her shopping basket was on the bench beside her. Her eyes were closed tight. This time Florrie did not disturb her. She walked by quietly and went home to the apartment. She would marry Reg, she decided. They would buy a house with a garden on the other side of the river, have puppies, kittens. Distractions, but she would enjoy them. Was there still time for a child? Not if she was sensible.

On her way upstairs, she stopped off on the fifth floor. Someone new had already moved into Mrs. Cornish's apartment. Had Perce and Ida taken her to live with them? Probably not. After all, would she?

Oh, she was already old, old. If she looked in her mirror, she was sure she would see Mrs. Cornish's face.

Responding Personally

1. Should Florrie have tried helping Mrs. Cornish more than she did? Did she fail the old woman? Talk about your ideas with a partner.
2. Describe how you might spend your eightieth birthday.

Responding Critically

3. How does Florrie feel when Mrs. Cornish first starts visiting? How do her feelings toward the old woman change as the story unfolds? What causes the change?
4. In each section of the story, the author reveals Mrs. Cornish's decreasing ability to look after herself. With a partner, make

a point-form chart, reviewing the story's six parts and summarizing what each part reveals. In your view, is Mrs. Cornish in need of supervised care? Explain.

5. For paragraph answer: Why does the story finish with Florrie's point of view? What conflict does Florrie experience in this final part of the story? What has Mrs. Cornish's fate made Florrie realize?
6. For a story to be effective, every detail must add to its development. Explain what the following details add to the meaning of the story:
   a) the excess furniture in Mrs. Cornish's apartment
   b) the fact that Mrs. Cornish once ran a boarding house where the highrise now stands
   c) Mrs. Cornish's habit of fumbling with her mother's amethyst brooch
   d) the painting by Florrie's uncle
   e) Mrs. Cornish's sitting at the cenotaph in autumn.

Responding Creatively

7. In a paragraph, describe your impressions of an elderly person you know—such as a neighbour or a grandparent. Share your paragraph with a partner before submitting it to classmates for evaluation.
8. Make a storyboard for one scene in the story.

Problem-Solving/Decision-Making

9. In a letter to the editor of your local newspaper, suggest some ways in which your community might improve the quality of life for the elderly.

UNIT FOUR

Setting and Atmosphere

When we tell stories, many of us start with information about where and when the events took place. The story opening may be factual, giving us a few details about the setting as in the following case: "Yesterday when I was on my way home from school, I stopped at the store across the street from the park." Or the story beginning may be dramatic, giving details about the atmosphere as well as the setting as in the following: "It was just after midnight and no other sounds could be heard except my own footsteps as I hurried down the dark alley." Either way, when we tell a story, we need to help our listeners picture the events by giving them an idea of the setting—the time and place of the story.

Our own stories—and we each have many based on our personal experiences—are set in a variety of locations and time periods. These details may be nothing more than a short description of the place and time. If we ever have struggled against elements of the environment, such as cold, heat, or turbulent water, however, we probably want to create a setting that is the source of the conflict in our story or the main reason for the story.

Details about the setting are important because they help create the atmosphere of a story. Recall a time when you walked home late at night and felt nervous as you passed dark entranceways and listened to the wind rustling in nearby bushes—or was it the wind? As you tell this story of your experience, your details about the place and time work together to prompt a sense of nervousness in your listeners. In the same way, the setting of a story can stir in readers an emotional reaction that will make the story more memorable and meaningful to them.

The stories that follow offer three very different descriptions of setting and atmosphere, and characters' experiences of them. The first story, “A Mountain Journey,” presents a life-and-death conflict in a hostile environment. The second story, “Afrika Road” presents the struggle of a road as people in conflict move from one location to another. The third story, “The Veldt,” combines a futuristic setting with a sinister atmosphere in the story of a fanciful world one family has created. These three stories help readers appreciate the significance of setting and atmosphere in relation to the events that develop in a story.

And as he looked back, while still sliding forward with the momentum of his descent, the ice broke beneath him.

Howard O'Hagan
A Mountain Journey

Dave Conroy, whose breath had hung stubby icicles on his moustache, paused upon the very summit of the pass. He tucked his ski poles under his arms, leaned upon them, sinking their discs into the creaking snow, and while he rested there panting, the cold was an old man's fingers feeling craftily through his clothes.

He was tired. He was so tired that his mouth was dry with the taste of salt. He was more tired than he had any right to be, and Hoodoo cabin on Hoodoo Creek, where he could pass the night, was still five miles away. It was downhill now though, downhill all the way. For the first time during the long day he could stand back on his skis and let them carry him where he wished to go. Since daylight he had come twenty miles and climbed four thousand feet from the lower Smokey to the pass. On his shoulders he had lifted upwards with him at every step his pack of food for another five days on the trail, his blankets, axe and fifty pounds of fur for the market—the result of six weeks' trapping on the head of the Jackpine. At every step too, he had broken trail and his skis had sunk a foot in the new snow, white and soft as flour.

He knew as he stood on the summit that he should have made camp two miles back in the timber and crossed the divide in the morning. Back there he had passed a fine spruce tree, its wide branches sweeping low, so that close against its trunk, cradled in its roots, he had seen the brown mossy ground where no snow had fallen and where he might have made his fire and spread his blankets. That tree, like a strong and lonely woman, called to his weary body to stop. But two hours of daylight remained and he went on.

He thought that if he had waited another two weeks to come out, till March, the snow would have had a crust for travelling, the days would have been longer, the cold less severe. Anyway, a

man was a fool to travel alone in the mountains, especially with a heavy pack, bucking a fresh fall of snow. A man when he was alone would travel too far. He would travel till he could travel no more, for the mere sake of travelling, when a day or two's delay in the time of his arrival made no difference at all.

Still, the worst was over. It was downgrade now to the railroad, eighty miles of trail along the Snake Indian River with cabins to put up at every night. No more siwashing under trees, burrowing four feet down in the snow for a place to sleep, with a snow-covered tree sweating in the heat of his fire, dripping water on his neck and dampening his blankets. Not that under such conditions a man slept very much. It was too cold. If he slept, his fire slept with him. It was better to stay awake, his blankets over his shoulders, and a pile of wood handy at his elbow.

Up there on the pass it was very still. No wind blew and his breath rose white and yellow before him. His heart thumped and hissed in his breast, and the silence about him as he listened became a roar as if it were the roar of the grey earth rolling on through space and time. Behind him his ski trail stretched a few feet, two black lines with the webbed marks of his ski poles pacing beside them. Mist, like the shadow of universal darkness on the treeless summit, moved about him, searched every crevice of the mountain land, roamed in great billows, formed in the blindness and suffering of eternal homelessness.

Conroy turned his skis down the slope before him. He was beginning to feel like a ghost on an abandoned planet and he wanted to see the works of man about him once again. He longed for the sight of a cabin, a clearing in the forest, yellow flaming blazes on trees beside the trail. Snow, flung up by the prow of his skis, pattered lightly against his thighs and as he hummed downwards he thought of supper—brown curled bacon, brown bannock, rice with butter melting on it, tea red and strong as rum.

The rolling alplands, a white sea frozen into weary immobility, became a broken parkland and he made long sweeping turns around clumps of spruce and balsam. Dark green trees came out of the thinning mist towards him, touched him with outflung branches, passed in a flutter and flurry of snow-dust. The cold wind against his face, the loud wind howling in crescendo by his ears, the flow of wind that pressed his trousers tight against his legs, gave him back strength as he exulted in the rush of his descent. Tears smarted in his eyes and through them he saw the landscape opaque and blurred as though it were vibrating to the speed of his passage.

He swung to the right in a wide telemark that threw snow in his face, swept down an open meadowland where the black tips of willows showed between two walls of timber, dropped off a cutbank to the frozen river, glanced a moment over his shoulder at the curved beauty of his ski trail on the hill above, curved and smooth and thin, like the tracing of a pen upon the snow.

And as he looked back, while still sliding forward with the momentum of his descent, the ice broke beneath him. It broke with a low muffled reverberation, startling as if the river had spoken. The snow rifted about him, the points of his skis dropped down. He was thrown forward and to save himself from falling on his face plunged down his hands. His pack slipped forward upon the back of his head and held him. The river was shallow and his hands rested on its gravelled bottom. He saw the snow melt around his wrists and flow into the top of his mittens, searing the flesh of his wrists like flame. He saw dark water streaming in furrows by his wrists and before he staggered upright again heard water tinkling over pebbles, murmuring, protesting, running downhill between ice and pebbles to the Arctic Ocean.

Conroy was too weak to rise beneath the pack. He rolled over upon his side, slipped the thongs of the ski poles from his wrists, dropped his pack on the snow beside him, raised himself and lifted his skies from the water. Water had seeped down his socks into his boots and his feet were cold and clammy.

He had fallen into an air hole. Probably a warm spring entered into the river nearby and above it the ice was thin. That was a peril of winter travel. But the rivers, levelled with ice and snow, were the winter highways of the mountains, and a man, when he could, travelled along them in preference to breaking a heavy trail in the timber.

Conroy unclamped his skis, upended them, and stood knee-deep in the snow. Already the water on them had crusted into ice. He took off his sodden mittens, opened his clasp-knife, and tried to scrape the ice from the skis' running surface. He knew what he should do. He should stop, make a fire, dry his hand and feet, change his socks and mittens. But it was late. It would mean si-washing for another night underneath a tree. A biting wind was driving the mist back up the valley and the sun westering behind the ranges threw long feeble shadows across the snow. He was less than three miles from the cabin, and the promise of its warmth and comfort would not let him stop.

He wriggled his toes in his boots. They were cold, but perhaps, he thought, not wet. Only his ankles and heels seemed wet. If he hurried he could make it. He slammed his right foot back into his ski iron, bent down to clamp it to his ski, but his fingers already were numbed with the cold. He rose again, thrashed his arms about his shoulders, bringing the blood tingling to their tips, opened his pack sack and found a pair of woollen inner mitts. He would have to get along without the moose-hide outers. They were already frozen stiff and he put them into his pack.

His skis clamped to his feet at last, he hoisted his pack, took his poles and started off, hunching his toes to keep the circulation going. Ice on the bottom of the skis dragged heavily in the snow, but he fought against it, pushing on his poles, knowing that speed was his one means of escape from the cold hand of wilderness that pressed against his back.

The long white avenue of the river opened before him, lined on either side by tall spruce trees. The wind was rising with the sun-down. It whipped snow against his face, cut through the weave of his woollen mitts, set the forest moaning beside him. He bent his head against it, his eyes on the black tapering points of his skis, ducking and dodging through the snow. It was as though he were engaged in some fantastic pursuit with those ski points always just beyond him, their tight cheeks pulled back into a cadaverous grin.

His shoulder muscles, as he lunged against the ski poles, bulged as though they would burst their skin, ached until their pain became a cry within him. His legs moving back and forth beneath him seemed tireless. They could go on forever and he no longer knew whether he could stop them. The pain in his shoulders was the only reality of his existence and his body was no more than the shape of agony and effort crawling through the twilight, across the long shadows of spruce trees laid upon the snow.

He came up from the river through the timber into the cabin clearing. But no log walls rose to greet him. No closed door waited for his touch to open. He stood in the middle of the clearing where the cabin had been, hemmed about by swaying pine trees, pine trees that swayed as the wind sighed through them. Snow, as if it had garnered light from the day, cast upwards a shadowless glow and Conroy saw close to him the black butts of congregated logs, a corner of the cabin, draped in white, rising lonely as a monument left by men a hundred years ago.

Since he had passed that way, fire had gutted the cabin. A few log ends remained above ground. It was as though the cabin had subsided into the snow that rose like a slow inundation to cover it. A beggared moon from behind a grey rack of clouds wandered in the sky above the earth's desolation and in its light he perceived on the slope above him, where the fire had leaped from the cabin, stiff, branchless trees, like a parade of skeletons climbing up the mountainside.

The next cabin was at Blue Creek, eighteen miles down the river. It was farther than he had strength to go. He would camp here in the clearing where the cabin had been burned. He slipped his pack off and reached toward it for the handle of his axe to cut kindling, making shavings for his fire. His fingers refused to bend. Protected only by the woollen mitts, they were stiff with the cold. He beat his hands about his shoulders, flung his arms in circles, took off his mittens and rubbed his hands together in the snow, but felt no blood pulsing in his fingertips.

He bit his fingers. They were cold and white and unresponsive as a dead man's. His right thumb tingled; when he rubbed his hands across his face, his beard bristled on the palms. It was only his fingers that defied him. He had been a fool. He should have made a fire when he fell through the ice, and should have spent the night three miles up the river under a tree. He had always said that mountain travel was not dangerous if a man knew how to take care of himself. Any man who froze his hands or feet had only himself to blame ...

As he stood there, stamping on his skis, his arms flapping at his sides, he remembered Duncan Macdonald, who trapped in the Beaver River country and who had walked thirty miles to the railroad on frozen feet to have them amputated by the doctor. Because he could trap no more, Macdonald had opened a cobbler's shop in Jasper to make boots he could no longer wear himself, and Conroy saw him now at his bench, laughing, not saying anything at all, just laughing, his red face wrinkled as he nodded his heavy bald head and laughed.

Conroy decided that his hands were not frozen, his feet, which he could no longer feel in his boots, not frozen. He needed fire to warm them. Since he could not make kindling, since he could not bend his fingers around the shaft of his axe, he would set a tree afire, he would set the forest in a blaze around him and warm himself in its midst. Small dry twigs under a spruce tree would flame like paper. Putting his left wrist over his right, he forced his right hand into the pocket where he carried his match-safe. He pried it out and it fell into the snow at his feet. He spread his skis and leaned down to pick it up. He poked his hands into the snow. They were like two sticks of wood on the ends of his arms and shoved the safe deeper and farther from him. He stooped lower still and finally, pressing it between his wrists, filched it out. He held it there before him, at arm's length, a round tin cylinder that contained the red flame and blustering smoke of fire. His right thumb, still moving to his command, pressed it into his palm, but his fingers would not catch it, would not twist it open. They would not bring the match-safe to him. They held it from him. If they would only bend, those fingers. If they would understand when he spoke to them.

He looked about him as if he would find the realities of his situation in the snow at his feet. He was eighty miles from the railroad, a journey of four days. Unable to light a fire, without warmth or food, he would never make it. His fingers were frozen. His feet probably were frozen too. He had one chance. Across the river from Hoodoo Creek where he stood, a high pass led over into the Moose River. Frank MacMoran trapped up there and had his cabin on Terrace Creek. From Hoodoo Creek to Terrace Creek was no more than ten miles. If he left his pack behind, he could probably pull through. He had never finished a day in the mountains yet without another ten miles up his sleeve.

His back was wet with sweat from carrying the pack, and he shivered with the cold. The cold was nibbling at him, at his nose, at his cheeks, crawling like a wet thing across his back. He forced his hands into his mittens, shoved them through the thongs of his ski poles and started off. He did not need to grasp the poles tightly. His hands rested upon the thongs which bore the weight he put upon them. His fingers did not pain him. He felt no sensations in them at all and his feet might have been pieces of wood strapped within his ski boots.

He crossed the river and angled up the slope towards the ridge that lay between him and the Moose. When he came out of the timber, the moon threw his shadow on the snow, a shadow faltering and stooped as if at any minute it might leave him, send him on alone to go shadowless through the moonlight. His shadow became a burden, something he pulled beside him in the snow.

He climbed high above the timber. The wind blew before him the long ends of the red neckerchief that he wore tied around the collar of his mackinaw, and near him the moon threw the outlines of a peak black upon the snow, black as ink seeping through the snow. Conroy paused a moment, leaned against a snow bank, sank down into it and rested.

How good to rest! How soft and warm the snow! There was the valley below him, empty in the moonlight—the clearing in the forest, timber that looked small and black as marsh grass. Across from him was a line of peaks thrust up against the sky, notched and jagged as if old bones, half-covered with the snow, littered their crests. To his left was the pass, a low saddle in the mountains, where he crossed in the afternoon.

From below, somewhere in the forest, a wolf howled.

Conroy glanced upwards over his shoulder. He had still six hundred feet to climb to the ridge above the Moose, above the cabin at Terrace Creek where MacMoran waited. MacMoran would take him in, feed him, make a fire for him to sit beside. He gathered his muscles together, summoned his strength that was slipping from him like a loosened garment. Then he lay back for another moment, to rest.

When he opened his eyes again, the moon had gone. The red sun, topping the range across the valley, shone upon him. His neckerchief flapped in the wind on the snow beside his cheek. He had slipped lower, fallen over upon his side, his face turned towards the route he had followed where his half-obliterated ski trail led down to the timber, the stunted spruce and balsam that seemed to be on their way towards him.

He heard horse bells. It was winter and no horses were within a hundred miles. He heard streaming river water. He heard a wide brown river running over mossy boulders between low banks of grass and willow. Across the valley he saw a cottage he had never seen before—a white cottage, low-roofed, with green trees beside it and an open door.

Then he remembered that he was on his way to MacMoran's cabin on Terrace Creek. MacMoran would be waiting for him. He tried to rise, but his arms stayed still at his side. Snow had drifted over them. A weight was on them that he could not lift. They were heavy with the burden of their own inertia. Snow like a blanket covered his body and the wind blew snow against his face.

For a moment he thought again of Macdonald who had brought his frozen feet to the railroad. Macdonald frowned and shook his head, opened his mouth and spoke some words that Conroy could not hear.

They would come and get him, Conroy thought—Macdonald, MacMoran, someone would come and get him. They were camped now down by Hoodoo cabin. They would see his trail and come and get him. He would lie for a while and wait.

Later, the pale cold sun was high in the sky. It shone full upon him. But the light of the sun was dim, as if a brighter light shone from behind it and the sunlight was its shadow. He could not see across the valley now, where the white cottage with the open door and the green trees had been. The world was growing small, dying slowly in the darkness of the sunlight.

Responding Personally

1. What could Dave Conroy have done differently to survive?
2. With a partner, describe a time when you were very cold or lost in the wilderness.

Responding Critically

3. With a classmate, list the obstacles and setbacks faced by Conroy. What mistakes does he make? What caused his death?
4. At what point does the reader know the protagonist is in serious trouble and not likely to reach MacMoran's cabin? Explain.
5. How does the author create suspense, atmosphere, and intrigue?
6. What is the purpose of the story? Does it have a "message" for the reader? Share your ideas with others.

Responding Creatively

7. Using details from the story, sketch a scene which might be selected by a magazine to illustrate this story.
8. With a partner, develop a game based on this story that focuses on survival in the wilderness. Use details of Conroy's experiences in your game instructions.

Problem-Solving/Decision-Making

9. On the Internet or at a library, research *hypothermia*. Then give a talk to the class presenting facts about hypothermia and ways to avoid it.

Bullets made of hot breath and noise and spit reverberated in the air.

Don Mattera

Afrika Road

There are many roads and lanes and streets and byways in South Africa but none quite like me, Afrika Road.

Each black township, no matter where it is situated, has an Afrika Road of its own. We are commonly known as the Tar Road, and those who create the townships and make the laws also conceive roads like us to facilitate the easy mobility of military and police vehicles. Usually there is a single road into and out of the townships. But the black people say they are not fools. They know the real motives of the rulers.

I am long and black and beautiful like a flat piece of licorice. Some folks say that my beauty has been spoiled by the obstinate white line because it cuts into my melanic majesty. But the line, like the Law of the land, slithers defiantly from the sun's bedroom in the west where I begin, to Masphala Hill in the east—a hot seat of conferred power which houses the Bantu Council Chambers and the police station.

I, Afrika Road, know and have endured the weight and pressure of all sorts of moving objects: human, animal, and mechanical. I groaned under the grinding repression of many military convoys and police brass bands that led the mayoral processions to the Hill of power. I also witness weddings and childbirths, and hear the noise of speeding police cars and ambulances, as well as the plaintive burial dirges of people weeping mournfully as they go. I hear the cries of the lonely of heart and I am familiar with the bustling din of jubilant folk whose merriment and laughter permeate the ghetto.

I am a mighty road.

All the dusty and soil-eroded lanes and streets converge on my body, bringing throngs of panting people. And I hold them all on my sturdy lap, year in and year out, birth in and death out.

There was a time when I was a teeming caldron of "people on the boil." The flames of mob anger and violence had razed the homes and businesses of men and women who threw in their lot and collaborated with the rulers of the land, or so the people said. Policemen and suspected informers and agents were brutally attacked. Some were even put to the torch. Yet amid the fear and frenzy of the marching and shouting masses, I, Afrika Road, caught glimpses of genuine gaiety on the people's faces. It was a welcome paradox, nonetheless. Humor and anger marching side by side.

That day the marchers varied in shade between chocolate-brown and shining ebony and fair apricot-skinned activists—rich characteristics for the human centipede that took to the streets.

It was one of many dates anywhere on the calendar of black resistance. The masses had heaved and swayed and breathed in the wild wind of their own passions. Occasionally the main body of the crowd opened up its floodgates and swallowed several hundreds of new protesters and their assortment of crude weaponry: sticks, stones, axes, homemade swords, knives, and dustbin lids. Four hundred people poured out of Mpanza Street; five hundred from Matambo and a half-drunk dozen from Sis Sonti's *shebeen*. The call to arms had a magnetic pull even for the imbibers. A soldier was a soldier drunk or sober, or so the leaders said. What mattered most were numbers.

Between Goba and Zamani streets, where the elite owner-built homes stand proud and indifferent, only three youngsters joined the swelling ranks. The Mkhuku Shanty Town dwellers mingled early in their hundreds. The march gained momentum. Men, women, children, and the fire-eating T-shirted comrades—soldiers without uniforms or conventional armory—were carried along the hard journey of insurrection, aware that death waited for them on Masphala Hill.

And they sang defiantly.

Songs that challenged and mocked the armed keepers of the Hill, that hated Hill which many blacks see as one of countless links in the chain of bondage and humiliation, or so the people said. Those who served in state-created institutions and sought and found sanctuary inside the high barbed-wire walls of the Hill were branded puppets, sellouts, and *mpimpi*—the word used to describe informers and fifth-columnists.

I, Afrika Road, bore that maddened crowd as it rambled and swayed in the fervor of revolt toward the Hill of confrontation where hundreds of heavily armed battalions of soldiers, policemen, and the local greenbean law enforcers kept vigil. Their automatic weapons caught flashes of the shimmering gold and orange sunrays that blistered from a cloudless sky. The singing reached fever pitch when a group of chanting, flag-carrying militant youth took the lead toward the waiting death machine.

The songs spoke of imminent battle and vengeance, and of the people's hunger for liberation. Songs which exhorted the Bothas to release Nelson Mandela and all the other political prisoners. There were martial strophes which alluded to the impending acquisition of AK-47s, Scorpion automatic pistols, and bazooka rocket launchers. Then came the electrifying *toi-toi* war dance, which appeared to penetrate and possess the very souls of the marchers. It seemed to me that the masses yearned to touch the faces of death or victory—whichever came first.

The *toi-toi* is a ritual dance which people have come to fear and hate or love and revere depending on which side of the political trenches a person stood—with the masses or the "masters."

A truly awe-inspiring sight, thousands of angry and anxious feet in an exuberant display of bravado and daring. Up and down, back and forth; then forward and ever onward—spilling the froth and sweat of excitement on my black brow.

And I, Afrika Road, saw schoolchildren in khaki uniforms raise their wooden guns at the law enforcers on the Hill. Bullets made of hot breath and noise and spit reverberated in the air. "We are going to kill them in the company of their children," the khaki-clad warriors chanted. Death waited for them on the Hill as the crowd drew closer and closer. It would be the final confrontation: more than sixty thousand marchers heading for the showdown. Heading for freedom, or so they said.

You see it in their youthful eyes: a readiness to feel the familiar thud on the chest, and to hear the cracking of bone and the ripping of lung as the firepower of the law enforcers makes its forced entry and exit through the weak dissident flesh.

You see it in the failing young arms of the children—always the children in the firing line—in tattered clothes or in school uniforms; T-shirted or bared chests; you see their hands fisted in the ardor of transient emotions; lives destined never to fully experience the essence of a natural childhood. You see them.

And I, Afrika Road, have seen them rise and then run undaunted against the ill wind; falling but emerging anew through sheaves of resisting corn—giving the earth life that genuine life might be reborn—or so I have heard the people's poets say during the many long marches.

A late-model car zoomed out of a small, nondescript lane between Zwide and Zwane streets. The well-dressed, well-fed driver, a wealthy local businessman and Bantu councilor, was en route to his sanctuary on Masphala Hill. He swerved noisily onto me. People dived to safety as the expensive imported vehicle screeched, skidded, and smoked at the wheels, and burned me.

Someone shouted, "*Mpimpi!*"

The human telegraph wire relayed the hated word and echoed it against the blue sky. The leaders in front got the message, stopped, and gave their backs to the waiting militia, who instinctively raised their guns at the ready in anticipation of attack.

The laminated windows of the car sagged under the weight of flying rock. Some of the youngsters jumped on it and smashed the front windshield. The terror-stricken man sat openmouthed, immobilized by his fear of death.

And I, Afrika Road, watched, knowing the fateful outcome. I have witnessed it too many times.

"Mpimpi!"

The chilling indictment rang out one final time.

A huge stone crushed the driver's skull. His eyes blinked and then went blank. Blood poured from his ears, nose, and mouth. They dragged him out. The back of his head cracked against me. I drank his blood just like I tasted the blood of many before him, and many more to come.

It is the law and the legacy.

Someone rolled a tire. Someone lifted a petrol can. Someone struck a match on Afrika Road …

Responding Personally

1. What is your reaction to the road narrating the story?
2. In pairs, discuss what you already know about African history and culture that is reflected in the story.

Responding Critically

3. With a partner, review three or more sights Afrika Road saw over the time of this story. Relate two characteristics you learned about the road.
4. What is the likely motivation of the protesters? Why are they so angry? What role does setting play in this conflict?
5. Quote two examples of African dialect words. What do they mean? What do they add to the story?
6. In a good short story, all the details provided are necessary and helpful. Choose three details from the story and explain how each is necessary to the story.

Responding Creatively

7. With a partner, write a rap song version of "Afrika Road." Be prepared to perform it for the class.
8. In a paragraph, write the stream of consciousness thoughts of a road where you live.

Problem-Solving/Decision-Making

9. Do some library research on Nelson Mandela, one of the real-life people mentioned in the story. Who is he and why has he been so important in South African history? What approaches has he used to solve racism and to heal his country's "wounds"? Write a report about his work and present it to the class.

The lions stood looking at George and Lydia Hadley with terrible green-yellow eyes.

Ray Bradbury

The Veldt

"George, I wish you'd look at the nursery."

"What's wrong with it?"

"I don't know."

"Well, then."

"I just want you to look at it, is all, or call a psychologist in to look at it."

"What would a psychologist want with a nursery?"

"You know very well what he'd want." His wife paused in the middle of the kitchen and watched the stove busy humming to itself, making supper for four.

"It's just that the nursery is different now than it was."

"All right, let's have a look."

They walked down the hall of their soundproofed Happylife Home, which had cost them thirty thousand dollars installed, this house which clothed and fed and rocked them to sleep and played and sang and was good to them. Their approach sensitized a switch somewhere and the nursery light flicked on when they came within ten feet of it. Similarly, behind them, in the halls, lights went on and off as they left them behind, with a soft automaticity.

"Well," said George Hadley.

They stood on the thatched floor of the nursery. It was forty feet across by forty feet long and thirty feet high; it had cost half again as much as the rest of the house. "But nothing's too good for our children," George had said.

The nursery was silent. It was empty as a jungle glade at hot high noon. The walls were blank and two-dimensional. Now, as George and Lydia Hadley stood in the center of the room, the walls began to purr and recede into crystalline distance, it seemed, and

presently an African veldt appeared, in three dimensions; on all sides, in color reproduced to the final pebble and bit of straw. The ceiling above them became a deep sky with a hot yellow sun.

George Hadley felt the perspiration start on his brow.

"Let's get out of the sun," he said. "This is a little too real. But I don't see anything wrong."

"Wait a moment, you'll see," said his wife.

Now the hidden odorophonics were beginning to blow a wind of odor at the two people in the middle of the baked veldtland. The hot straw smell of lion grass, the cool green smell of the hidden water hole, the great rusty smell of animals, the smell of dust like a red paprika in the hot air. And now the sounds: the thump of distant antelope feet on grassy sod, the papery rustling of vultures. A shadow passed though the sky. The shadow flickered on George Hadley's upturned, sweating face.

"Filthy creatures," he heard his wife say.

"The vultures."

"You see, there are the lions, far over, that way. Now they're on their way to the water hole. They've just been eating," said Lydia. "I don't know what."

"Some animal." George Hadley put his hand up to shield off the burning light from his squinted eyes. "A zebra or a baby giraffe, maybe."

"Are you sure?" His wife sounded peculiarly tense.

"No, it's a little late to be sure," he said, amused. "Nothing over there I can see but cleaned bone, and the vultures dropping for what's left."

"Did you hear that scream?" she asked.

"No."

"About a minute ago?"

"Sorry, no."

The lions were coming. And again George Hadley was filled with admiration for the mechanical genius who had conceived this room. A miracle of efficiency selling for an absurdly low price. Every home should have one. Oh, occasionally they frightened you with their clinical accuracy, they startled you, gave you a twinge, but most of the time what fun for everyone, not only your own son and daughter, but for yourself when you felt like a quick jaunt to a foreign land, a quick change of scenery. Well, here it was!

And here were the lions now, fifteen feet away, so real, so feverishly and startlingly real that you could feel the prickling fur on your hand, and your mouth was stuffed with the dusty upholstery smell of their heated pelts, and the yellow of them was in your eyes like the yellow of an exquisite French tapestry, the yellows of lions and summer grass, and the sound of the matted lion lungs exhaling on the silent noontide, and the smell of meat from the panting, dripping mouths.

The lions stood looking at George and Lydia Hadley with terrible green-yellow eyes.

"Watch out!" screamed Lydia.

The lions came running at them.

Lydia bolted and ran. Instinctively, George sprang after her. Outside, in the hall, with the door slammed, he was laughing and she was crying, and they both stood appalled at the other's reaction.

"George!"

"Lydia! Oh, my dear poor sweet Lydia!"

"They almost got us!"

"Walls, Lydia, remember; crystal walls, that's all they are. Oh, they look real, I must admit—Africa in your parlor—but it's all dimensional, superreactionary, supersensitive color film and mental tape film behind glass screens. It's all odorophonics and sonics, Lydia. Here's my handkerchief."

"I'm afraid." She came to him and put her body against him and cried steadily. "Did you see? Did you *feel*? It's too real."

"Now, Lydia ..."

"You've got to tell Wendy and Peter not to read any more on Africa."

"Of course—of course." He patted her.

"Promise?"

"Sure."

"And lock the nursery for a few days until I get my nerves settled."

"You know how difficult Peter is about that. When I punished him a month ago by locking the nursery for even a few hours—the tantrum he threw! And Wendy too. They *live* for the nursery."

"It's got to be locked, that's all there is to it."

"All right." Reluctantly he locked the huge door. "You've been working too hard. You need a rest."

"I don't know—I don't know," she said, blowing her nose, sitting down in a chair that immediately began to rock and comfort her. "Maybe I don't have enough to do. Maybe I have time to think too much. Why don't we shut the whole house off for a few days and take a vacation?"

"You mean you want to fry my eggs for me?"

"Yes." She nodded.

"And darn my socks?"

"Yes." A frantic, watery-eyed nodding.

"And sweep the house?"

"Yes, yes—oh, yes!"

"But I thought that's why we bought this house, so we wouldn't have to do anything?"

"That's just it. I feel like I don't belong here. The house is wife and mother now and nursemaid. Can I compete with an African veldt? Can I give a bath and scrub the children as efficiently or quickly as the automatic scrub bath can? I can not. And it isn't just me. It's you. You've been awfully nervous lately."

"I suppose I have been smoking too much."

"You look as if you didn't know what to do with yourself in this house, either. You smoke a little more every morning and drink a little more every afternoon and need a little more sedative every night. You're beginning to feel unnecessary too."

"Am I?" He paused and tried to feel into himself to see what was really there.

"Oh, George!" She looked beyond him, at the nursery door. "Those lions can't get out of there, can they?"

He looked at the door and saw it tremble as if something had jumped against it from the other side.

"Of course not," he said.

At dinner they ate alone, for Wendy and Peter were at a special plastic carnival across town and had televised home to say they'd be late, to go ahead eating. So George Hadley, bemused, sat watching the dining-room table produce warm dishes of food from its mechanical interior.

"We forgot the ketchup," he said.

"Sorry," said a small voice within the table, and ketchup appeared.

As for the nursery, thought George Hadley, it won't hurt for the children to be locked out of it awhile. Too much of anything isn't good for anyone. And it was clearly indicated that the children had been spending a little too much time on Africa. That sun. He could feel it on his neck, still, like a hot paw. And the lions. And the smell of blood. Remarkable how the nursery caught the telepathic emanations of the children's minds and created life to fill their every desire. The children thought lions, and there were lions. The children thought zebras, and there were zebras. Sun—sun. Giraffes—giraffes. Death and death.

That last. He chewed tastelessly on the meat that the table had cut for him. Death thoughts. They were awfully young, Wendy and Peter, for death thoughts. Or, no, you were never too young, really. Long before you knew what death was you were wishing it on someone else. When you were two years old, you were shooting people with cap pistols.

But this—the long, hot African veldt—the awful death in the jaws of a lion. And repeated again and again.

"Where are you going?"

He didn't answer Lydia. Preoccupied, he let the lights glow softly on ahead of him, extinguished behind him as he padded to the nursery door. He listened against it. Faraway, a lion roared.

He unlocked the door and opened it. Just before he stepped inside, he heard a faraway scream. And then another roar from the lions, which subsided quickly.

He stepped into Africa. How many times in the last year had he opened this door and found Wonderland, Alice, the Mock Turtle, or Aladdin and his Magical Lamp, or Jack Pumpkinhead of

Oz, or Dr. Doolittle, or the cow jumping over a very real-appearing moon—all the delightful contraptions of a make-believe world. How often had he seen Pegasus flying in the sky ceiling, or seen fountains of red fireworks, or heard angel voices singing. But now, this yellow hot Africa, this bake oven with murder in the heat. Perhaps Lydia was right. Perhaps they needed a little vacation from the fantasy which was growing a bit too real for ten-year-old children. It was all right to exercise one's mind with gymnastic fantasies, but when the lively child mind settled on *one* pattern ...? It seemed that, at a distance, for the past month, he had heard lions roaring, and smelled their strong odor seeping as far away as his study door. But, being busy, he had paid it no attention.

George Hadley stood on the African grassland alone. The lions looked up from their feeding, watching him. The only flaw to the illusion was the open door through which he could see his wife, far down the dark hall, like a framed picture, eating her dinner abstractedly.

"Go away," he said to the lions.

They did not go.

He knew the principle of the room exactly. You sent out your thoughts. Whatever you thought would appear.

"Let's have Aladdin and his lamp," he snapped.

The veldtland remained; the lions remained.

"Come on, room! I demand Aladdin!" he said.

Nothing happened. The lions mumbled in their baked pelts.

"Aladdin!"

He went back to dinner. "The fool room's out of order," he said. "It won't respond."

"Or——?"

"Or what?"

"Or it *can't* respond," said Lydia, "because the children have thought about Africa and lions and killing so many days that the room's in a rut."

"Could be."

"Or Peter's set it to remain that way."

"*Set* it?"

"He may have got into the machinery and fixed something."

"Peter doesn't know machinery."

"He's a wise one for ten. That I.Q. of his——"

"Nevertheless——"

"Hello, Mom. Hello, Dad."

The Hadleys turned. Wendy and Peter were coming in the front door, cheeks like peppermint candy, eyes like bright blue agate marbles, a smell of ozone on their jumpers from their trip in the helicopter.

"You're just in time for supper," said both parents.

"We're full of strawberry ice cream and hot dogs," said the children, holding hands. "But we'll sit and watch."

"Yes, come tell us about the nursery," said George Hadley.

The brother and sister blinked at him and then at each other. "Nursery?"

"All about Africa and everything," said the father with false joviality.

"I don't understand," said Peter.

"Your mother and I were just traveling through Africa with rod and reel: Tom Swift and his Electric Lion," said George Hadley.

"There's no Africa in the nursery," said Peter simply.

"Oh, come now, Peter. We know better."

"I don't remember any Africa," said Peter to Wendy. "Do you?"

"No."

"Run see and come tell."

She obeyed.

"Wendy, come back here!" said George Hadley, but she was gone. The house lights followed her like a flock of fireflies. Too late, he realized he had forgotten to lock the nursery door after his last inspection.

"Wendy'll look and come tell us," said Peter.

"She doesn't have to tell *me*. I've seen it."

"I'm sure you're mistaken, Father."

"I'm not, Peter. Come along now."

But Wendy was back. "It's not Africa," she said breathlessly.

"We'll see about this," said George Hadley, and they all walked down the hall together and opened the nursery door.

There was a green, lovely forest, a lovely river, a purple mountain, high voices singing, and Rima, lovely and mysterious, lurking in the trees with colorful flights of butterflies, like animated bouquets, lingering on her long hair. The African veldtland was gone. The lions were gone. Only Rima was here now, singing a song so beautiful that it brought tears to your eyes.

George Hadley looked in at the changed scene. "Go to bed," he said to the children.

They opened their mouths.

"You heard me," he said.

They went off to the air closet, where a wind sucked them like brown leaves up the flue to their slumber rooms.

George Hadley walked through the singing glade and picked up something that lay in the corner near where the lions had been. He walked slowly back to his wife.

"What is that?" she asked.

"An old wallet of mine," he said.

He showed it to her. The smell of hot grass was on it and the smell of a lion. There were drops of saliva on it, it had been chewed, and there were blood smears on both sides.

He closed the nursery door and locked it, tight.

In the middle of the night he was still awake and he knew his wife was awake. "Do you think Wendy changed it?" she said at last, in the dark room.

"Of course."

"Made it from a veldt into a forest and put Rima there instead of lions?"

"Yes."

"Why?"

"I don't know. But it's staying locked until I find out."

"How did your wallet get there?"

"I don't know anything," he said, "except that I'm beginning to be sorry we bought that room for the children. If children are neurotic at all, a room like that——"

"It's supposed to help them work off their neuroses in a healthful way."

"I'm starting to wonder." He stared at the ceiling.

"We've given the children everything they ever wanted. Is this our reward—secrecy, disobedience?"

"Who was it said, 'Children are carpets, they should be stepped on occasionally'? We've never lifted a hand. They're insufferable—let's admit it. They come and go when they like; they treat us as if *we* are offspring. They're spoiled and we're spoiled."

"They've been acting funny ever since you forbade them to take the rocket to New York a few months ago."

"They're not old enough to do that alone, I explained."

"Nevertheless, I've noticed they've been decidedly cool toward us since."

"I think I'll have David McClean come tomorrow morning to have a look at Africa."

"But it's not Africa now, it's Green Mansions country and Rima."

"I have a feeling it'll be Africa again before then."

A moment later they heard the screams.

Two screams. Two people screaming from downstairs. And then a roar of lions.

"Wendy and Peter aren't in their rooms," said his wife.

He lay in his bed with his beating heart. "No," he said. "They've broken into the nursery."

"Those screams—they sound familiar."

"Do they?"

"Yes, awfully."

And although their beds tried very hard, the two adults couldn't be rocked to sleep for another hour. A smell of cats was in the night air.

"Father?" said Peter.

"Yes."

Peter looked at his shoes. He never looked at his father any more, nor at his mother. "You aren't going to lock up the nursery for good, are you?"

"That all depends."

"On what?" snapped Peter.

"On you and your sister. If you intersperse this Africa with a little variety—oh, Sweden perhaps, or Denmark or China——"

"I thought we were free to play as we wished."

"You are, within reasonable bounds."

"What's wrong with Africa, Father?"

"Oh, so now you admit you have been conjuring up Africa, do you?"

"I wouldn't want the nursery locked up," said Peter coldly. "Ever."

"Matter of fact, we're thinking of turning the whole house off for about a month. Live sort of a carefree one-for-all existence."

"That sounds dreadful! Would I have to tie my own shoes instead of letting the shoe tier do it? And brush my own teeth and comb my hair and give myself a bath?"

"It would be fun for a change, don't you think?"

"No, it would be horrid. I didn't like it when you took out the picture painter last month."

"That's because I wanted you to learn to paint all by yourself, son."

"I don't want to do anything but look and listen and smell; what else *is* there to do?"

"All right, go play in Africa."

"Will you shut off the house sometime soon?"

"We're considering it."

"I don't think you'd better consider it anymore, Father."

"I won't have any threats from my son!"

"Very well." And Peter strolled off to the nursery.

"Am I on time?" said David McClean.

"Breakfast?" asked George Hadley.

"Thanks, had some. What's the trouble?"

"David, you're a psychologist."

"I should hope so."

"Well, then, have a look at our nursery. You saw it a year ago when you dropped by; did you notice anything peculiar about it then?"

"Can't say I did; the usual violences, a tendency toward a slight paranoia here or there, usual in children because they feel persecuted by parents constantly, but, oh, really nothing."

They walked down the hall. "I locked the nursery up," explained the father, "and the children broke back into it during the night. I let them stay so they could form the patterns for you to see."

There was a terrible screaming from the nursery.

"There it is," said George Hadley. "See what you make of it."

They walked in on the children without rapping.

The screams had faded. The lions were feeding.

"Run outside a moment, children," said George Hadley. "No, don't change the mental combination. Leave the walls as they are. Get!"

With the children gone, the two men stood studying the lions clustered at a distance, eating with great relish whatever it was they had caught.

"I wish I knew what it was," said George Hadley. "Sometimes I can almost see. Do you think if I brought high-powered binoculars here and——"

David McClean laughed dryly. "Hardly." He turned to study all four walls. "How long has this been going on?"

"A little over a month."

"It certainly doesn't *feel* good."

"I want facts, not feelings."

"My dear George, a psychologist never saw a fact in his life. He only hears about feelings; vague things. This doesn't feel good, I tell you. Trust my hunches and my instincts. I have a nose for something bad. This is very bad. My advice to you is to have the whole damn room torn down and your children brought to me every day during the next year for treatment."

"Is it that bad?"

"I'm afraid so. One of the original uses of these nurseries was so that we could study the patterns left on the walls by the child's mind, study at our leisure, and help the child. In this case, however, the room has become a channel toward—destructive thoughts, instead of a release away from them."

"Didn't you sense this before?"

"I sensed only that you had spoiled your children more than most. And now you're letting them down in some way. What way?"

"I wouldn't let them go to New York."

"What else?"

"I've taken a few machines from the house and threatened them, a month ago, with closing up the nursery unless they did their homework. I did close it for a few days to show I meant business."

"Ah, ha!"

"Does that mean anything?"

"Everything. Where before they had a Santa Claus now they have a Scrooge. Children prefer Santas. You've let this room and this house replace you and your wife in your children's affections. This room is their mother and father, far more important in their lives than their real parents. And now you come along and want to shut it off. No wonder there's hatred here. You can feel it coming out of the sky. Feel that sun. George, you'll have to change your life. Like too many others, you've built it around creature comforts. Why, you'd starve tomorrow if something went wrong in your kitchen. You wouldn't know how to tap an egg. Nevertheless, turn everything off. Start new. It'll take time. But we'll make good children out of bad in a year, wait and see."

"But won't the shock be too much for the children, shutting the room up abruptly, for good?"

"I don't want them going any deeper into this, that's all."

The lions were finished with their red feast.

The lions were standing on the edge of the clearing watching the two men.

"Now *I'm* feeling persecuted," said McClean. "Let's get out of here. I never have cared for these damned rooms. Make me nervous."

"The lions look real, don't they?" said George Hadley. "I don't suppose there's any way——"

"What?"

"—that they could *become* real?"

"Not that I know."

"Some flaw in the machinery, a tampering or something?"

"No."

They went to the door.

"I don't imagine the room will like being turned off," said the father.

"Nothing ever likes to die—even a room."

"I wonder if it hates me for wanting to switch it off?"

"Paranoia is thick around here today," said David McClean. "You can follow it like a spoor. Hello." He bent and picked up a bloody scarf. "This yours?"

"No." George Hadley's face was rigid. "It belongs to Lydia."

They went to the fuse box together and threw the switch that killed the nursery.

The two children were in hysterics. They screamed and pranced and threw things. They yelled and sobbed and swore and jumped at the furniture.

"You can't do that to the nursery, you can't!"

"Now, children."

The children flung themselves onto a couch, weeping.

"George," said Lydia Hadley, "turn on the nursery, just for a few moments. You can't be so abrupt."

"No."

"You can't be so cruel."

"Lydia, it's off, and it stays off. And the whole damn house dies as of here and now. The more I see of the mess we've put ourselves in, the more it sickens me. We've been contemplating our mechanical, electronic navels for too long. My God, how we need a breath of honest air!"

And he marched about the house turning off the voice clocks, the stoves, the heaters, the shoe shiners, the shoe lacers, the body scrubbers and swabbers and massagers, and every other machine he could put his hand to.

The house was full of dead bodies, it seemed. It felt like a mechanical cemetery. So silent. None of the humming hidden energy of machines waiting to function at the tap of a button.

"Don't let them do it!" wailed Peter at the ceiling, as if he was talking to the house, the nursery. "Don't let Father kill everything." He turned to his father. "Oh, I hate you!"

"Insults won't get you anywhere."

"I wish you were dead!"

"We were, for a long while. Now we're going to really start living. Instead of being handled and massaged, we're going to *live*."

Wendy was still crying and Peter joined her again. "Just a moment, just one moment, just another moment of nursery," they wailed.

"Oh, George," said the wife, "it can't hurt."

"All right—all right, if they'll only just shut up. One minute, mind you, and then off forever."

"Daddy, Daddy, Daddy!" sang the children, smiling with wet faces.

"And then we're going on a vacation. David McClean is coming back in half an hour to help us move out and get to the airport. I'm going to dress. You turn the nursery on for a minute, Lydia, just a minute, mind you."

And the three of them went babbling off while he let himself be vacuumed upstairs through the air flue and set about dressing himself. A minute later Lydia appeared.

"I'll be glad when we get away," she sighed.

"Did you leave them in the nursery?"

"I wanted to dress too. Oh, that horrid Africa. What can they see in it?"

"Well, in five minutes we'll be on our way to Iowa. Lord, how did we ever get in this house? What prompted us to buy a nightmare?"

"Pride, money, foolishness."

"I think we'd better get downstairs before those kids get engrossed with those damned beasts again."

Just then they heard the children calling, "Daddy, Mommy, come quick—quick!"

They went downstairs in the air flue and ran down the hall. The children were nowhere in sight. "Wendy? Peter!"

The ran into the nursery. The veldtland was empty save for the lions waiting, looking at them. "Peter, Wendy?"

The door slammed.

"Wendy, Peter!"

George Hadley and his wife whirled and ran back to the door.

"Open the door!" cried George Hadley, trying the knob. "Why, they've locked it from the outside! Peter!" He beat at the door. "Open up!"

He heard Peter's voice outside, against the door.

"Don't let them switch off the nursery and the house," he was saying.

Mr. and Mrs. George Hadley beat the door. "Now, don't be ridiculous, children. It's time to go. Mr. McClean'll be here in a minute and …"

And then they heard the sounds.

The lions on three sides of them, in the yellow veldt grass, padding through the dry straw, rumbling and roaring in their throats.

The lions.

Mr. Hadley looked at his wife and they turned and looked back at the beasts edging slowly forward, crouching, tails stiff.

Mr. and Mrs. Hadley screamed.

And suddenly they realized why those other screams had sounded familiar.

"Well, here I am," said David McClean in the nursery doorway. "Oh, hello." He stared at the two children seated in the center of the open glade eating a little picnic lunch. Beyond them was the water hole and the yellow veldtland; above was the hot sun. He began to perspire. "Where are your father and mother?"

The children looked up and smiled. "Oh, they'll be here directly."

"Good, we must get going." At a distance Mr. McClean saw the lions fighting and clawing and then quieting down to feed in silence under the shady trees.

He squinted at the lions with his hand up to his eyes.

Now the lions were done feeding. They moved to the water hole to drink.

A shadow flickered over Mr. McClean's hot face. Many shadows flickered. The vultures were dropping down the blazing sky.

"A cup of tea?" asked Wendy in the silence.

Responding Personally

1. Who do the characters of Peter and Wendy remind you of?
2. Will artificial environments such as the nursery be possible in the future? Exchange ideas with a partner.

Responding Critically

3. Reread the story locating three details that suggest a futuristic setting. How does this setting influence the characters' lives?
4. Describe the goals and motivation of Peter and Wendy. What will they likely do with David? Why?
5. What foreshadowing is there of George and Lydia's fate? Give examples of ways in which they raise their children badly.
6. In a paragraph, write about Bradbury's view of technology and the nature of children.

Responding Creatively

7. With a partner, design a home page for the store that sells this nursery.
8. Write a movie review of the video version of this story from *The Ray Bradbury Theater* (Atlantis).

Problem-Solving/Decision-Making

9. Debate conservative versus liberal child-raising methods. After the debate, resolve what are your own views and write them in a personal response.

UNIT FIVE

Point of View

Many times in a typical week we will likely share a story about what happened during our day, or we may retell an entertaining story related to us by a friend or a family member. Whether we are telling a story about ourselves or someone else, we are limited in the details we include because we are limited by what details we know. In a story we tell about ourselves, we can add our own thoughts and feelings, which add information for our listeners. We may not know, however, about the thoughts and feelings of some of the people we talk about. If we do know their thoughts and feelings because we have talked to them and heard them express their feelings, we can decide what details to include in our telling of the story that will help make it interesting and meaningful.

The teller of a story or the narrator, whether in life or literature, sees the story through his or her own eyes and interprets the events for the readers. This special point of view gives a story its unity and helps the reader to see the events and details from a particular perspective. Told through the eyes of an observant narrator, a story will come alive and draw the reader into that story world.

The selections in this unit offer readers experiences from three different points of view. The first story, "Penny in the Dust," presents details in the first person, letting us know the feelings of the narrator. The second story, "A Little Beaded Bag," is told from a third person perspective—through the eyes of the wife of the household. The third story, "Sculpin," offers an omniscient point of view that allows readers to see a range of characters and viewpoints on the story's events.

"Pete," he said, "you needn'ta hid. I wouldn'ta beat you."

Ernest Buckler

Penny in the Dust

My sister and I were walking through the old sun-still fields the evening before my father's funeral, recalling this memory or that—trying, after the fashion of families who gather again in the place where they were born, to identify ourselves with the strange children we must have been.

"Do you remember the afternoon we thought you were lost?" my sister said. I did. That was as long ago as the day I was seven, but I'd had occasion to remember it only yesterday.

"We searched everywhere," she said. "Up in the meeting-house, back in the blueberry barrens—we even looked in the well. I think it's the only time I ever saw Father really upset. He didn't even stop to take the oxen off the wagon tongue when they told him. He raced right through the chopping where Tom Reeve was burning brush, looking for you—right through the flames almost; they couldn't do a thing with him. And you up in your bed, sound asleep!"

"It was all over losing a penny or something, wasn't it?" she went on, when I didn't answer. It was. She laughed indulgently. "You were a crazy kid, weren't you?"

I was. But there was more to it than that. I had never seen a shining new penny before that day. I'd thought they were all black. This one was bright as gold. And my father had given it to me.

You would have to understand about my father, and that is the hard thing to tell. If I say that he worked all day long but never once had I seen him hurry, that would make him sound like a stupid man. If I say that he never held me on his knee when I was a child and that I never heard him laugh out loud in his life, it would make him sound humorless and severe. If I said that whenever I'd be reeling off some of my fanciful plans and he'd come into the kitchen and I'd stop short, you'd think that he was distant and that in some kind of way I was afraid of him. None of that would be true.

There's no way you can tell it to make it sound like anything more than an inarticulate man a little at sea with an imaginative child. You'll have to take my word for it that there was more to it than that. It was as if his sure-footed way in the fields forsook him the moment he came near the door of my child's world and that he could never intrude on it without feeling awkward and conscious of trespass; and that I, sensing that but not understanding it, felt at the sound of his solid step outside, the child-world's foolish fragility. He would fix the small spot where I planted beans and other quickly-sprouting seeds before he prepared the big garden, even if the spring was late; but he wouldn't ask me how many rows I wanted and if he made three rows and I wanted four, I couldn't ask him to change them. If I walked behind the load of hay, longing to ride, and he walked ahead of the oxen, I couldn't ask him to put me up and he wouldn't make any move to do so until he saw me trying to grasp the binder.

He, my father, had just given me a new penny, bright as gold.

He'd taken it from his pocket several times, pretending to examine the date on it, waiting for me to notice it. He couldn't offer me *anything* until I had shown some sign that the gift would be welcome.

"You can have it if you want it, Pete," he said at last.

"Oh, thanks," I said. Nothing more. I couldn't expose any of my eagerness either.

I started with it, to the store. For a penny you could buy the magic cylinder of "Long Tom" popcorn with Heaven knows what glittering bauble inside. But the more I thought of my bright penny disappearing forever into the black drawstring pouch the storekeeper kept his money in, the slower my steps lagged as the store came nearer and nearer. I sat down in the road.

It was that time of magic suspension in an August afternoon. The lifting smells of leaves and cut clover hung still in the sun.

The sun drowsed, like a kitten curled up on my shoulder. The deep flour-fine dust in the road puffed about my bare ankles, warm and soft as sleep. The sound of the cowbells came sharp and hollow from the cool swamp.

I began to play with the penny, putting off the decision. I would close my eyes and bury it deep in the sand; and then, with my eyes still closed, get up and walk around, and then come back to search for it. Tantalizing myself, each time, with the excitement of discovering afresh its bright shining edge. I did that again and again. Alas, once too often.

It was almost dark when their excited talking in the room awakened me. It was Mother who had found me. I suppose when it came dusk she thought of me in my bed other nights, and I suppose she looked there without any reasonable hope but only as you look in every place where the thing that is lost has ever lain before. And now suddenly she was crying because when she opened the door there, miraculously, I was.

"Peter!" she cried, ignoring the obvious in her sudden relief, "*where* have you been?"

"I lost my penny," I said.

"You lost your penny ...? But what made you come up here and hide?"

If Father hadn't been there, I might have told her the whole story. But when I looked up at Father, standing there like the shape of everything sound and straight, it was like daylight shredding the memory of a silly dream. How could I bear the shame of repeating before him the childish visions I had built in my head in the magic August afternoon when almost anything could be made to seem real, as I buried the penny and dug it up again? How could I explain that pit-of-the-stomach sickness which struck through the whole day when I had to believe, at last, that it was really gone? How could I explain that I wasn't really hiding from *them*? How, with the words and the understanding I had then, that this was the only possible place to run from that awful feeling of loss?

"I lost my penny," I said again. I looked at Father and turned my face into the pillow. "I want to go to sleep."

"Peter," Mother said, "it's almost nine o'clock. You haven't had a bite of supper. Do you know you almost scared the *life* out of us?"

"You better get some supper," Father said. It was the only time he had spoken.

I never dreamed that he would mention the thing again. But the next morning when we had the hay forks in our hands, ready to toss out the clover, he seemed to postpone the moment of actually leaving for the field. He stuck his fork in the ground and brought in another pail of water, though the kettle was chock full. He took out the shingle nail that held a broken yoke strap together and put it back in exactly the same hole. He went into the shed to see if the pigs had cleaned up all their breakfast.

And then he said abruptly: "Ain't you got no idea where you lost your penny?"

"Yes," I said, "I know just about."

"Let's see if we can't find it," he said.

We walked down the road together, stiff with awareness. He didn't hold my hand.

"It's right here somewhere," I said. "I was playin' with it, in the dust."

He looked at me, but he didn't ask me what game anyone could possibly play with a penny in the dust.

I might have known he would find it. He could tap the alder bark with his jack-knife just exactly hard enough so it wouldn't slit but so it would twist free from the notched wood, to make a whistle. His great fingers could trace loose the hopeless snarl of a fishing line that I could only succeed in tangling tighter and tighter. If I broke the handle of my wheelbarrow ragged beyond sight of any possible repair, he could take it and bring it back to me so you could hardly see the splice if you weren't looking for it.

He got down on his knees and drew his fingers carefully through the dust, like a harrow; not clawing it frantically into heaps as I had done, covering even as I uncovered. He found the penny almost at once.

He held it in his hand, as if the moment of passing it to me were a deadline for something he dreaded to say, but must. Something that could not be put off any longer, if it were to be spoken at all.

"Pete," he said, "you needn'ta hid. I wouldn'ta beat you."

"*Beat* me? Oh, Father! You didn't think that was the reason ...?" I felt almost sick. I felt as if I had struck *him*.

I had to tell him the truth then. Because only the truth, no matter how ridiculous it was, would have the unmistakable sound truth has, to scatter that awful idea out of his head.

"I wasn't hidin', Father," I said, "honest. I was ... I was buryin' my penny and makin' out I was diggin' up treasure. I was makin' out I was findin' gold. I didn't know what to *do* when I lost it, I just didn't know where to *go* ..." His head was bent forward, like mere listening. I had to make it truer still.

"I made out it was gold," I said desperately, "and I—I was makin' out I bought you a mowin' machine so's you could get your work done early every day so's you and I could go in to town in the big automobile I made out I bought you—and everyone'd turn around and look at us drivin' down the streets ..." His head was perfectly still, as if he were only waiting with patience for me to finish. "*Laugh*in' and *talk*in'," I said. Louder, smiling intensely, com*pell*ing him, by the absolute conviction of some true particular, to believe me.

He looked up then. It was the only time I had ever seen tears in his eyes. It was the only time in my seven years that he had ever put his arm around me.

I wondered, though, why he hesitated, and then put the penny back in his own pocket.

Yesterday I knew. I never found any fortune and we never had a car to ride in together. But I think he knew what that would be like, just the same. I found the penny again yesterday, when we were getting out his good suit—in an upper vest pocket where no one ever carries change. It was still shining. He must have kept it polished.

I left it there.

Responding Personally

1. Does Pete do the right thing in returning the penny to his father's pocket? Why or why not? Exchange ideas with a partner.
2. Write about a memory in which you and a parent, relative, or guardian understood that you love each other without actually saying it in words.

Responding Critically

3. What key information about the plot and characters is given in the story's first sentence?
4. With a partner, review the main misunderstanding around the lost penny.
5. The penny in this story is symbolic. In a group, discuss what it represents to the father when he first gives it to his son and then what it represents to him after it is found. What does the penny represent to the son when he first receives it? What does it means to him at the end of the story?
6. Theoretically, Buckler could have presented the story from the father's or sister's point of view. Does he make the right choice in presenting the story from Pete's perspective? Explain.

Responding Creatively

7. Write the eulogy Pete gives at his father's funeral.
8. With a partner, prepare a children's book version of this story for six to seven year olds.

Problem-Solving/Decision-Making

9. Think of a relative or family friend who needs your love and attention. Write a letter of appreciation to him or her.

She whispered, "Haven't I got a perfect right to find out if I've got a thief in the house?"

Morley Callaghan
A Little Beaded Bag

When young Mrs. Evans came in at dinner time and noticed that the little white beaded bag she had tossed on the chair in the bedroom that afternoon was gone, she was sure Eva, the maid, had taken it. The girl, helping her clean out the chest of drawers in the bedroom, had found the bag she'd put aside a year ago because the little white beads had come loose around the metal clasp. Mrs. Evans had hesitated, remembering the night she'd carried it to a party after returning from Europe, and then she'd sighed, knowing she would never get it fixed, and tossed it at the rubbish on the paper spread out on the floor.

"My, it's pretty, isn't it?" Eva said as she picked it up. Mrs. Evans took it from her, looked at it, wondering if she ought to keep it after all, and undecided, tossed it onto the bedroom chair.

When her husband who was a young lawyer came home, she might never have mentioned the bag if he hadn't sat down sullenly and refused to speak to her. They had quarreled the night before. They had been married only a year, but in the last few months there seemed to be some tension and strain between them that puzzled her and made them sometimes want to hurt each other terribly. When she saw him hiding gloomily behind the newspaper, she was touched and regretted the quarrel: she wanted to tell him that he was wrong about last night, that he was crazy if he thought she really expected him to drop all his old friends, and that she understood he could still be in love with her and yet want to have some freedom of his own.

"David," she said, a little timidly, "David, I was thinking—"

"I'm tired," he said in a surly voice, and when he didn't even look at her, she suddenly remembered that he liked Eva and used to ask her questions about her family on the farm, so she said, casually, "You may be interested to know Eva stole that beaded bag of mine."

"What's that? What bag?" he exclaimed.

"You know the one, the one I had a year ago."

"Why, the kid wouldn't touch it," he said sharply. "You know that as well as I do. She's a fine kind. You've been trying for weeks to find some little flaw in her, and you've had to admit, yourself, you couldn't. Don't start picking away at her."

It seemed so unjust that he should challenge her, and as they faced each other, she said bitterly, "I'm not picking at her or you. I'm telling you a fact. The bag was there this morning and it's gone."

"I don't think she's taken it, that's all," he said.

"We can soon find out if you doubt it," she said.

"Well, I certainly doubt it."

"Of course you do," she replied, "of course you do. You mean you doubt my judgment about everything. Well, I'll show you," she said, and she smiled very brightly at him.

She went into the kitchen where Eva was getting the dinner ready. She sat down and watched the girl's soft hair, and her plump young shape as she moved around. The girl grew nervous and began to smooth her apron and looked scared. Mrs. Evans kept watching her, never smiling, never speaking, and when Eva reddened and half-turned, she offered no explanation. Eva could no longer stand the shrewd, calm, knowing expression in Mrs. Evan's eyes, and she turned nervously. "Is there anything wrong, ma'am?" she asked.

"Do you remember that purse this morning?"

"Yes, ma'am. Weren't you going to throw it out?"

"You know I wasn't throwing it out, Eva."

"Well—"

"Somebody took it."

"Maybe I threw it out in the trash barrel," she said, and she looked at Mrs. Evans, as if pleading with her to make some friendly little remark about it being unimportant and that she was sure the bag would turn up.

But Mrs. Evans, seeing how disturbed the girl was, said easily, "Eva, would you run down to the drug store and get me some cigarettes?" and she smiled.

"Right now?" the girl asked, reluctantly.

"Yes, right now, please."

Eva was frightened and sullen, trying to make some kind of plan as she stood there. Then she turned to go back to her room, but Mrs. Evans called sharply, "You don't need your coat, Eva. Just go as you are." They faced each other, and for just a moment, Eva resisted an antagonism she did not understand. In the last month she had hardly spoken to either Mr. or Mrs. Evans. When she heard them quarreling at night she was afraid they would call her to bring them a drink, and her hand would tremble and Mrs. Evans would be impatient, and then Eva would hear Mr. Evans defending her good-naturedly. But now, she nodded obediently and went out in a wild rush, for she was scared of losing her job.

Mrs. Evans went straight to the girl's bedroom and David followed, scowling at her. She trembled with excitement going through Eva's dresser drawer, pushing aside little boxes of cheap powder, an old photograph of Eva's father, who was a big, poorly dressed man, a few letters which she held in her hand wondering if Eva had talked about her; and then with her heart pounding with excitement as she listened for the sound of the girl's footsteps, and feeling strangely like a thief herself, she went to the cupboard and pulled out the girl's club bag and fished through the nightdress, the old tattered prayer-book, the love story magazine. At the bottom was the damaged white beaded bag. She stood up triumphantly and smiled at her husband who turned away as if he was sick. As she followed him into the livingroom, the door slammed and the girl came rushing in, flushed, her eyes full of apprehension, and she handed Mrs. Evans the cigarettes.

"Thanks, Eva," she said, a little coldly, and the girl reddened and wheeled around and went into her bedroom.

"Well, now, was I right? Am I right about something?" she said to David.

"No, you weren't right," he said quietly.

"It was in her bag, you saw it yourself," she said. "Don't you believe your own eyes?" But it bothered her terribly that he only stared at her. She whispered, "Haven't I got a perfect right to find out if I've got a thief in the house? What are you staring at me for, wasn't I right?" He sat there as if she were a stranger who puzzled him.

Then they heard Eva calling, "Mrs. Evans, could I speak to you a moment, please?" and she came in, holding out the dainty little white purse, trying to smile innocently. But her eyes showed how completely helpless she felt with the little white purse, as if something bright and elusive had betrayed her.

"You found it," Mrs. Evans said uneasily.

"Yes, I found it, don't you see," she whispered, nodding her head eagerly, begging Mrs. Evans to just take the purse and not make her a liar.

"Where did you find it?" Mrs. Evans asked.

"In the trash barrel," Eva said, never taking her eyes off Mrs. Evans's face. "I must have picked it up with some papers and things. I remembered I put all those things you wanted thrown out in one pile, and I thought I might have picked it up, too, and I went and looked. I'm very sorry, Mrs. Evans."

"Why, thanks, Eva, thanks," Mrs. Evans said, hesitating, and when the girl hesitated, too, and then went, she hoped it was all over, but when she turned to David, he was more distressed than ever. She grew ashamed, yet she fought against this shame and said, indignantly, "What's the matter with you? She took it and she knows I caught her."

"Maybe you're satisfied," he whispered.

"I don't know what you mean," she said.

"You know she didn't intend to take it. You know you made her a thief. You humiliated the kid, you took away her self-respect," he said, coming close to her as if he was going to shake her. "My Lord, if you knew what you looked like going through the kid's things."

"I didn't, I didn't," she whispered.

"You're ruthless when you get started—just like I told you last night, utterly ruthless."

"It's got nothing to do with us," she said angrily.

"Yes, it has. You're still at me, and it doesn't matter about the kid," he said. "Keep it up, keep getting everything tighter till it snaps and then we'll hate each other."

He looked so disappointed that she put out her hand and touched him on the arm. "I didn't mean it like that. I knew I was right, that's all."

"Sure, you were right. You're right about so many things," he said, shaken a little because she looked frightened, and he muttered, "I don't know what's the matter with you," and he swung away from her and she heard him going out.

She sat down with her hands up to her face. As she looked down at the little beaded bag, so small and unimportant, it seemed that day after day with her doubts and discontent she did a whole succession of little things that were right but they only cheapened her life and David's, as she had just cheapened Eva's.

She got up and hurried to Eva's bedroom and called anxiously, "Eva, may I come in?"

Eva was sitting on the bed, sullen and fearful, waiting.

"Eva—this purse," Mrs. Evans said, holding it up and trying to smile. Eva looked away, her face red. "I only wanted to see if it could be fixed," Mrs. Evans said. "There are a few beads loose. You're good with a needle, aren't you? Couldn't you fix it up for yourself?"

"I don't know. It's awfully pretty, isn't it?" Eva said, taking it in her two hands and fingering it shyly, "It's terribly pretty."

"Take it, please take it," Mrs. Evans whispered, and Eva looked up astonished because Mrs. Evans had one hand up to her lips and though her voice was eager, her eyes were brimming with tears as if she were begging Eva to help her.

RESPONDING PERSONALLY

1. With a partner, compare notes on whether you feel sorry for Eva or Mrs. Evans.

2. In a paragraph, recall a time when you or someone you know was falsely accused of an action. What happened?

Responding Critically

3. In a group, brainstorm ideas about the different conflicts in the story. Summarize them in a paragraph.
4. What is Mrs. Evans' motivation in making an issue of the "stolen" beaded bag? Why does she change her approach at the end of the story? In your opinion, did she change as a result of her experience? Explain.
5. Why do you think Mr. Evans did not believe his wife's accusation? Was he right? Explain.
6. What do Eva's possessions show about her? Does she know what is really happening with her employers? Tell your ideas to a partner.

Responding Creatively

7. Write the stream of consciousness thoughts of Mrs. Evans during the story.
8. Compose your own short story about a thief who gets caught.

Problem-Solving/Decision-Making

9. If you were a marriage counsellor, what advice would you give to the Evans? Can their marriage be saved? Why or why not?

To her, the distant fish was an untidy blob stirring up buzzing flies.

Tom Dawe

Sculpin

It was a late, hot July in the cove. There seemed to be more power in the sun as the dry weeks wore on towards August. Mummified patterns of last month's caplin-scull rotted in the wire sunlight adding to the pungent smell rolling up from the landwash-maw each time the breeze veered in from the grounds. The warped, splintered plants of the community wharf leaned out towards the hazy infinity of open Atlantic.

For the past several warm nights, the moon had been round and full, sucking the passive tides to wind around the old boarded-up sheds near the oil edge of the land, and shining down on the floating tin-cans tinkling in the ground swell. Bits of wood, dead grass, scraps of cardboard and other refuse bobbed quietly in chain along the coast.

Nobody fished for a living here anymore. Most of the able men had gone outside the cove to work now that roads were bulldozed through to the coast. The children were bused several miles away to a larger school each day. The women cooked meals, looked at the clock and waited, listening to their radios; their days and nights of peering anxiously out over the old worn wharf were over. A few old men could be seen mumbling in and around the leaning sheds; sitting on the upturned boats and yarning away the time. Sometimes one of them could be seen, pipe between his teeth, dozing on a sunny rock or perched on an upturned tub out on the wharf. Often, as a couple of them seemed to argue, they gestured with pipe-stems and bony, tobaccoed fingers out towards the etched horizon of soaring gulls and back to the chain of houses set in the screes of the ancient shale cliffs.

Like living presences, the colour of salted fish-skin, the jagged cliffs slanted towards and above the little cove, ominous above the stove-pipes reaching up into the reeking air. The sun had been tipping their edges for thousands and thousands of years now, and many thousands of fish-eyed moons had lingered along the spiny row of crags above.

It was a Saturday morning. The sun had just splashed an edge of orange on the fish-skin cliffs as it started sweeping across the cove for another day. Not many people were out of bed yet. One old man swept bits of dried fish away from his doorstep and talked to the three cats lingering around his legs. A few chimneys showed wisps of kindling wood smoke swimming slowly up towards the leaning crags. In a very short time, the day would be clear and hot again.

Out on the wharf the sun began to pour down hotter on the pleading boards. Ethereal wires of heat danced on the heads of the eroded piles tapering away into the sharp refraction on a calm, shale surface. Odours of school-boy catches pierced up through the planks. Clusters of large, blue, bloated flies clung fitfully to a severed connor's head rotting in the morning stillness.

In the middle of the wharf, a big flounder, caught yesterday, lay belly-up in the sun. Its brown, mottled back bore the prints of foot-marks. A thin ribbon of blood trailed hardened from the stupid, swollen mouth and oozed down towards the large ancient boulders beneath the wharf.

One big fly staggered along the hard ribbon of blood and disappeared into the cold, blue stench beneath the planks.

Now that the sun was higher, the three old houses on the opposite side of the cove were sharply visible. Two of the simple structures were boarded up except for the upstairs windows of each, gaping deep like black sockets in weather bleached skulls. The other house belonged to Adam, the community drunkard. His door would not open for hours yet.

Alone, he slept off the effects of last night's bout at the tavern. From the wharf, Adam's house seemed leaning towards the ocean. In his yard, his ragged hip-rubbers were pinned on a kinked, drooping clothesline. With the first puff of morning wind in over the cove's bar, the feet of the old rubbers seemed to sway over the edges of the houses below on the next dusty lane. They seemed to walk, at intervals, above the blue ripple of the bay's surface.

Sometime after eleven that morning, a young boy of ten wandered down to the wharf. He scuffed the crude planking with his rubbers, kicking pebbles over the edge as he walked. As he moved, he unreeled a stiff wad of green fishing-line. At the end of the line, dangled a cruel, black wire fish-hook.

The boy tested the line's strength across his knee as he searched for a piece of bait. Screwing up his face in disgust, he kicked the rotten connor's head over the wharf and stared closely at the oily, orange-blue film trailing the mangled head towards the bottom. He turned and saw the dead flounder. With a blunt pocket-knife he hacked away seven small pieces of flesh from the dry, wrinkled back. Each piece, about the size of a man's thumbnail, looked blood-soaked white clinging to a jagged patch of leathery skin.

Satisfied with his seven pieces, the boy selected the smallest chunk of putrid flesh and fastened it securely on his hook. He kicked the carcass of flounder over the opposite side of the wharf, not stopping to watch it sink.

As his baited hook sank slowly into the water, the boy settled himself comfortably on the smoothest plank. Lying on his stomach, he peered at the bait sinking into the thick, salt buoyancy, into the myriad shadows where old piles sank into ocean floor.

An arrow of hungry connors darted after the drifting fibrous bait. The boy had difficulty keeping them away from the hook. Each time they charged, he moved the bait away turning several over on their sides and backs. These savage little fish were lovely, rusty, blue and shimmering net-like streaks weaving in and out on the sun's rays soaking fingers into the thick, salt water.

The boy was hoping for a tom-cod. Yesterday evening, he had seen a big, golden-brown seven-incher glide by the quiet piles. But such a fish was nowhere to be seen in this bright, direct sunlight today.

Growing bored with his fishing, the boy set his line around a rusty spike protruding out from the wharf's side. He stood up, stretched and yawned aloud. His stomach replied with a growl and made him think of lunch. He yawned again as he gazed across the cove. Adam, the drunkard, was emerging into the sunlight for the first time today. The boy heard his funny singing last night and laughed to himself as he remembered some of the lusty words. The boy waved to Adam, but the drunkard seemed too occupied to notice; he was leaning over his fence as if he wanted to vomit; he was peeling an orange and flipping the pieces over his shoulder.

"Hey, Charlie," called the drunkard, "leave that line hidden somewhere on the wharf when you leave. I'll catch a tom-cod later on for my breakfast tomorrow."

"Sure, Adam. Where do you want it put?" replied the boy only too willing to speak with the middle-aged man.

Adam ignored the boy again as he spit a couple of times over his fence into the neighbour's garden. Now the boy just watched him squeezing the orange between his shaking hands.

The boy had not seen the scuplin when it struck his bait.

As he turned away from the sight of Adam, the boy saw his catch. The large, bloated, grotesque fish had wobbled savagely up from the nether jungle of undulating shadows. It had gulped down the hook completely. The boy cursed softly and looked up at the drunkard who was now taking his rubbers off the clothes-line.

The sculpin twisted and thumped its black-mottled tail on the splinters of the indifferent plants. The monstrous mouth from which trailed the greenish line, gasped. It opened and closed making occasional sounds like somebody squeezing a piece of fruit. Bursting his line, and leaving the hook in the fish, the boy stamped on its horny head three times. Trailing his line after him, he headed home. The sculpin was left to die in the sun. It lay still now in the same spot, in the same slime and crusted blood pattern where the flounder had lain before.

The day wore into an afternoon. The ugly dead fish, anchored in the sun-baked slime, was now a prey for the flies. Big blue clusters walked fitfully over the horned head and hurried into the gaping mouth. They seemed excited as they quickly staggered over the bony rims of the lips and around the big circles of eyes that seemed to challenge the sun.

Three other boys visited the wharf in the early afternoon but none of them fished or stayed long. One of the boys kicked at the sculpin, tearing it from its fixed position in the sun. Screwing up his face, the boy nudged the fish over towards the edge of the wharf. He seemed intent on kicking the dead fish back into the ocean.

"Hey, fellers, look there's ol' Adam going up the lane. Let's catch him!" called one of the boys.

The boy quickly drew his rubber away from the sculpin and, cleaning his feet on the planks he chased his two friends up the lane. The three were laughing about the jokes Adam told them last night as he rolled around on the grass up by the potato-patch.

Later, some smaller boys watched an energetic tourist showing the sculpin to his wife, "Come and see the devil," he called to the shy boys who tried to act indifferent in the presence of a pretty, strange woman, pink-dressed with a flower in her yellow hair and keeping her distance from the smelly fish. She made a show of fuss, giggling and caressing her thighs as she smoothed her dress with long, white-gloved hands. She was getting some delight out of the view.

In the hour of suppertime, the old wharf was quiet except for the subdued buzzing of flies, the warm water lapping at the piles, and the distant cries of gulls high above the yawning mouth of the cove.

Just after supper, one of the old men strolled down on the wharf. He seemed to want to get as far out as possible. Perhaps now that he could go to sea no more, the wharf's projection was some consolation. It could take him at least a few feet from the shore each day. He sat musing on an old oil-stained tub near the head of the wharf. For ten minutes he blinked outward into the blue haze of distant ocean on the banks.

He looked down once and turned over the sculpin with his quivering walking-stick. The old man peered at the ugly face, the dead moon eyes, and paper-wrinkled belly. "Only the tail looks like a fish," he thought aloud to himself. He spit into the sea and watched the bubbles disperse. As he prepared to leave, the old fellow saw Adam going into his yard carrying a can of beans or something for his supper. The old man shook his head.

"The fool never fished in his life. He never looked like a fisherman," the old man thought aloud to himself.

After the old man left, a little girl stood near the shore and stared out at the dead fish on the wharf. She did not step on the planks because her mother had warned her to stay away from the wharf. She heard the radio playing up in her mother's kitchen and looked back over her shoulder at the wharf before she left. She never saw the sculpin's eyes still full and staring in the heat. To her, the distant fish was an untidy blob stirring up the buzzing flies.

Just before dark, a few boys fished for tom-cod near the shore, as the tide was high. The sculpin corpse still lay on the edge out on the end of the wharf.

The moon was pale orange and rising as they left.

Moonlight glistened in needles on the fish-skin wrinkles and filled the weird orbs of eyes bulging into the night. But nobody saw it.

Nobody saw drunk Adam slip and fall into the bay that night.

Nobody would ever know what really caused the dark figure out there in the moonlight to slip off the wharf.

A pristine undertow carried both man and sculpin slowly away from the undulating landwash of the sleeping village.

The full moon was sucking again on the obedient tides and reflecting down the hidden sun. Somewhere a fixed ball of sun was waiting for the cove to turn towards it again.

Responding Personally

1. Write down your thoughts and feelings as you read this story. Explain whether you were surprised by anything that happened in the story.
2. Describe local colour details that the story reveals about life in a harbour town.

Responding Critically

3. In a group, talk about the characters of the story. Is there a central character? What does each character contribute to the overview that is presented of the town?
4. What happens around the wharf at the end of the story? Is the reader prepared for the ending? Discuss your ideas with a partner.
5. Brainstorm ideas and then write your understanding of the story's theme and purpose.
6. Draw your own conclusions about the importance of the sculpin to the plot, characters, and conflicts of the story.

Responding Creatively

7. As Adam, write his last diary entry before he died.
8. Write a short story about the underlying reality of your own neighbourhood.

Problem-Solving/Decision-Making

9. As a local police officer, write a report on the disappearance of Adam and share your report in a group.

UNIT SIX

Irony and Symbol

Occasionally, a story provides a message on the surface but offers a deeper level of meaning through devices called irony and symbol. Symbolism is the use of an image, object, action, or person that acquires greater meaning and significance as the story develops. Irony is usually irony of situation, in which what happens is different from what the reader expects or what would seem appropriate to happen.

Both irony and symbol add depth to a story by compressing ideas. In other words, through using irony and symbol in stories, writers can say a lot in a few words. Irony is often used to provide humour, but it also serves to add depth of meaning to the story. Symbol is included primarily to compress ideas, but it adds deeper meaning to the selection as well. A story about a young girl, for example, in which she takes a bite from an apple is symbolic of the Garden of Eden and Eve's move into knowledge from innocence. Compressing ideas by using the symbol of the apple-eating adds meaning to the story without requiring the writer to go into detail about how the girl grows into knowledge from her former innocence.

The three stories in this unit provide different uses of symbol and irony. In the first story, "The Duel," there is dramatic irony in that the officer and reader know that the woman's son is dead yet she doesn't. In the second story, "Death of a Snow Machine," we see an aboriginal man who ironically abandons modern technology—his snowmobile—in favour of traditional ways. In the third story, "Flight," the granddaughter is linked with the pigeons symbolically throughout the story. In all three stories, we see ideas compressed by the writer's use of irony and symbolism.

"I do not need anything besides Vladimir; there is nothing dearer to me than his happiness."

Nicolai Teleshov
The Duel

It was early morning.

Vladimir Kladunov, a tall, graceful young man, twenty-two years of age, almost boyish in appearance, with a handsome face and thick, fair curls, dressed in the uniform of an officer and in long riding-boots, minus overcoat and cap, stood upon a meadow covered with new-fallen snow, and gazed at another officer, a tall, red-faced, moustached man, who faced him at a distance of thirty paces, and was slowly lifting his hand in which he held a revolver, and aimed it straight at Vladimir.

With his arms crossed over his breast and also holding in one hand a revolver, Kladunov, almost with indifference, awaited the shot of his opponent. His handsome young face, though a little paler than usual, was alight with courage, and wore a scornful smile. His dangerous position, and the merciless determination of his adversary, the strenuous attention of the seconds who silently stood at one side, and the imminence of death, made the moment one of terrible intensity, mysterious, solemn. A question of honour was to be decided. Everyone felt the importance of the question; the less they understood what they were doing, the deeper seemed the solemnity of the moment.

A shot was fired; a shiver ran through all. Vladimir threw his hands about, bent his knees, and fell. He lay upon the snow, shot through his head, his hands apart, his hair, face, and even the snow around his head covered with blood. The seconds ran toward him and lifted him; the doctor certified his death, and the question of honour was solved. It only remained to announce the news to the regiment and to inform, as tenderly and carefully as possible, the mother, who was now left alone in the world; for the boy who had been killed was her only son. Before the duel no one had given her even a thought; but now they all became very thoughtful. All knew and loved her, and recognised the fact that she must be prepared by degrees for the terrible news. At last Ivan Golubenko was chosen as most fit to tell the mother, and smooth out matters as much as possible.

Pelageia Petrovna had just risen, and was preparing her morning tea when Ivan Golubenko, gloomy and confused, entered the room.

"Just in time for tea, Ivan Ivanovitch!" amiably exclaimed the old lady, rising to meet her guest. "You have surely called to see Vladimir!"

"No, I—in passing by——" Golubenko stammered, abashed.

"You will have to excuse him, he is still asleep. He walked up and down his room the whole of last night, and I told the servant not to wake him, as it is a festival. But probably you come on urgent business?"

"No, I only stepped in for a moment in passing——"

"If you wish to see him, I will give the order to wake him up."

"No, no, do not trouble yourself!"

But Pelageia Petrovna, believing that he had called to see her son on some business or other, left the room, murmuring to herself.

Golubenko walked excitedly to and fro, wringing his hands, not knowing how to tell her the terrible news. The decisive moment was quickly approaching; but he lost control of himself, was frightened, and cursed the fate that had so mixed him up with the whole business.

"Now! How can a body trust you young people!" good-naturedly exclaimed Pelageia Petrovna to her visitor, entering the room. "Here I have been taking care not to make the least noise with the cups and saucers, and asking you not to wake my boy, and he has long ago departed without leaving a trace! But why do you not take a seat, Ivan Ivanovitch, and have a cup of tea? You have been neglecting us terribly lately!"

She smiled as with a secret joy, and added in a low voice:

"And we have had so much news during that time! Vladimir surely could not keep it secret. He must have told you all about it by now; for he is very straightforward and open-hearted, my Vladimir. I was thinking last night, in my sinful thoughts: 'Well, when my Vladimir paces the room the whole night, that means that he is dreaming of Lenochka!' That is always the case with him: if he paces the room the whole night, he will surely leave to-morrow. Ah, Ivan Ivanovitch, I only ask the Lord to send me this joy in my old age. What more does an old woman need? I have but one desire, one joy; and it seems to me I shall have nothing more to pray for after Vladimir and Lenochka are married. So joyful and happy it would make me! I do not need anything besides Vladimir; there is nothing dearer to me than his happiness."

The old lady became so affected that she had to wipe away the tears which came to her eyes.

"Do you remember?" she continued; "things did not go well in the beginning—either between the two or on account of the money. You young officers are not even allowed to marry without investments. Well, now everything has been arranged: I have obtained the necessary five thousand roubles for Vladimir, and they could go to the altar even to-morrow! Yes, and Lenochka has written such a lovely letter to me. My heart is rejoicing!"

Continuing to speak, Pelageia Petrovna took a letter out of her pocket, which she showed to Golubenko, and then put back again.

"She is such a dear girl! And so good!"

Ivan Golubenko, listening to her talk, sat as if on red-hot coals. He wanted to interrupt her flow of words, to tell her everything was at an end, that her Vladimir was dead, and that in one short hour nothing would remain to her of all her bright hopes; but he listened to her and kept silent. Looking upon her good, gentle face, he felt a convulsive movement in his throat.

"But why are you looking so gloomy to-day?" the old lady at last asked. "Why, your face looks as black as night!"

Ivan wanted to say "Yes! And yours will be the same when I tell you!" but instead of telling her anything, he turned his head away, and began to twirl his moustaches.

Pelageia Petrovna did not notice it, and wholly absorbed in her own thoughts, continued:

"I have a greeting for you. Lenochka writes that I must give Ivan Ivanovitch her kind regards, and ask him to come with Vladimir and pay her a visit. You know yourself how she likes you, Ivan Ivanovitch! No, it seems I cannot keep it to myself. I must show you the letter. Just see for yourself how loving and sweet it is."

And Pelageia Petrovna again fetched the packet of letters from her pocket, took from it a thin sheet, closely written, and unfolded it before Ivan Golubenko, whose face had become still gloomier. He tried to push away the extended note, but Pelageia Petrovna had already begun reading—

"DEAR PELAGEIA PETROVNA—When will the time arrive when I will be able to address you, not thus, but as my dear, sweet mother! I am anxiously awaiting the time, and hope so much that it will soon come that even now I do not want to call you otherwise than mother——"

Pelageia Petrovna lifted her head, and ceasing to read, looked at Golubenko with eyes suffused with tears.

"You see, Ivan Ivanovitch!" she added; but seeing that Golubenko was biting his moustaches, and that his eyes too were moist, she rose, placed a trembling hand up on his hair, and quietly kissed him on the forehead. "Thank you, Ivan Ivanovitch," she whispered, greatly moved. "I always thought that you and Vladimir were more like brothers than like ordinary friends. Forgive me. I am so very happy, God be thanked!"

Tears streamed down her cheeks, and Ivan Golubenko was so disturbed and confused that he could only catch in his own her cold, bony hand and cover it with kisses; tears were suffocating him, and he could not utter a word; but in this outburst of motherly love he felt such a terrible reproach to himself that he would have preferred to be lying himself upon the field, shot through the head, than to hear himself praised for his friendship by this woman who would in half an hour find out the whole truth. What would she then think of him? Did not he, the friend, the almost brother, stand quietly by when a revolver was aimed at Vladimir? Did not this brother himself measure the space between the two antagonists and load the revolvers? All this he did himself, did consciously; and now this friend and brother silently sat there without even having the courage to fulfil his duty.

He was afraid. At this moment he despised himself, yet could not prevail upon himself to say even one word. His soul was oppressed by a strange lack of harmony; he felt sick at heart and stifling. And in the meanwhile time flew. He knew it; and the more he knew it the less had he the courage to deprive Pelageia Petrovna of her few last happy moments. What should he say to her? How should he prepare her? Ivan Golubenko lost his head entirely.

He had already had time enough to curse in his thoughts all duels, all quarrels, every kind of heroism, and all kinds of so-called questions of honour, and he at last rose from his seat ready to confess or to run away. Silently and quickly he caught the hand of Pelageia Petrovna, and stooping over it to touch it with his lips, thus hid his face, over which a torrent of tears suddenly streamed down; impetuously, without another thought, he ran out into the corridor, seized his great-coat, and then went out of the house without a word.

Pelageia Petrofina looked after him with astonishment, and thought:

"He also must be in love, poor fellow. Well, that is their young sorrow—before happiness!" ...

And she soon forgot him, absorbed in her dreams of the happiness which seemed to her so inviolable and entire.

Responding Personally

1. Should the officer have told the dead man's mother the truth? Why do you think he couldn't? Do you think you would have been able to if you were in his place? Share your ideas with a partner.

2. Describe another duel that you have read about or viewed. What were the causes and results? How did they compare with those in this story?

Responding Critically

3. How does the author initially "trick" the reader? What is the real story in "The Duel"?
4. In your opinion, why could Ivan Golubenko not break the news to Vladimir's mother? Give evidence from the story to support your interpretation.
5. From what point of view is this story told? Why do you think the author chose this point of view? Who is the focal character? Exchange ideas in a group.
6. What is the atmosphere in the first half of the story? In the second half? Explain the reason for the contrast.

Responding Creatively

7. Assume that Ivan Golubenko goes home and decides to break the news to Vladimir's mother in writing. Prepare the letter he would write and read it to another student before submitting it to your teacher.
8. Compose a prequel in story form or in dialogue form about what led to the duel.

Problem-Solving/Decision-Making

9. Conduct a survey of your family and friends. The survey question is: "Is it better to tell someone a terrible truth than to leave that person in ignorant bliss?" Note your respondants' reasons for their opinions. Write your results to present to the class.

Hope those dogs can pull the sleigh, he thought.

Alfred Groulx

Death of a Snow Machine

Skeeptoe had followed the same ritual for forty years. As soon as the first good snow had fallen, he began loading his sleigh with winter supplies and made sure his snow machine had a full tank of gas and was in good working order. Just like him, the machine had seen better days. He had traded his dogs for the machine in 1968, but most of the time he wished that he hadn't. The machine needed to be repaired more often, and he hated to spend his hard-earned money on the repairs. If it were a dog he would have shot it by now and replaced it with a new, stronger one, but snow machines were too expensive now.

He doublechecked his trapping gear on the sleigh, then went back to the machine and tried to start it. He pulled the starting cord and the machine quickly roared to life—putta, putta, putta—and then it stalled just as quickly. Skeeptoe shook his head and went back into his cabin. There was still a fire in the stove, so he put on a kettle of water and waited for it to boil. He would have a cup of tea, then he would try and start the machine again. He sat and surveyed the cabin, gazing at the mementoes from his past; his eyes rested on a picture of his son, who had left the reserve a long time ago to rejoin civilization. He only returned to visit for two weeks each summer.

The kettle started to boil, and Skeeptoe watched the lid pop up and down. It reminded him of the summers when he used to dance at the powwows, but that was when he was a young man. A ray of sunlight shone through the cabin window and touched his cheek, dispersing his thoughts. He got up from the old bench he was sitting on and proceeded to make a cup of tea. He put in five spoons of sugar and a half a can of Carnation cream. He stirred the tea and tasted it. He smiled. Just the way I like it, he thought.

He finished his tea and left the cabin. He would try and start the machine again. He pulled out the choke and yanked on the starting cord. Putta, putta, putta. Skeeptoe kept his hand on the throttle for a few minutes just to make sure that the machine wouldn't stop. When he thought that the machine was finally warm enough he let go of the throttle. Putta, putta, putta. The machine died again. Well, time for another cup of tea, he thought as he went back into the cabin. He made his tea in the same fashion as before.

Skeeptoe sat down at his table. He looked at the vinyl red and white tablecloth and began to count the squares. He lost count and became immersed in his thoughts. Maybe it was good that his son had left the reserve. Trapping was hard now. There was not enough beaver, and the payment for a good pelt was low. It was not like this when he first started trapping. There were too many rules and regulations now. "Not financially feasible," he said out loud. He had heard the prime minister say that on the radio once. A knock on the door brought Skeeptoe back to his senses. "Come!" he shouted. The door creaked open and old Goocho stepped in.

"Still here?" asked Goocho.

"Ya, machine won't start," Skeeptoe replied.

"Dogs was always better. Least them could be put out of their misery when they got too old," Goocho said, laughing.

"Yep. I miss the old days too," Skeeptoe replied.

"Come, let me try and start the machine," Goocho said.

Skeeptoe finished his tea and followed Goocho out of the cabin. Goocho proceeded to check the machine, shaking his head as he checked the engine. Skeeptoe stood back smiling; he knew that Goocho didn't know anything about the machine. Goocho looked around at Skeeptoe and asked how to start the machine. After a short explanation, Goocho pulled out the choke and pulled on the starting cord. The machine whined into action. Goocho looked at Skeeptoe with a self-satisfied look on his face, as if to say, look, I got it going. Just as soon as Goocho let go of the throttle the infernal machine stopped again.

"May as well get some dogs, lots of stray dogs on the reserve. You just got to catch 'em. Bet they would be good workin' dogs," said Goocho as he left.

Skeeptoe went back into the cabin and sat down by the window. What Goocho said was true, but the question was how to catch the dogs. Skeeptoe sat and looked about his cabin. The big old white freezer caught his eye, and he got an idea. He went to the freezer and opened it. Best invention civilization ever came up with, he thought, winter in a box. He reached into the freezer and took out some moose meat and some trout that he had caught last summer. Then he went out to the old shed where the snow machine was kept in the summer and threw in the meat and fish. He turned and looked at the snow machine, shook his head and then went back into the cabin. He moved his bench close to the window so he could watch and see what would happen.

It was getting late when the first dog showed up. Skeeptoe, being a patient man, waited until there were seven or eight strong-looking dogs in the shed, then quietly slipped out of the cabin to the shed and closed the shed door, trapping the dogs inside. On his way back to the cabin, he picked up the dog harnesses that he had hung on the outside of his cabin when he had gotten rid of his dogs. These should be okay, he thought.

Inside the cabin he tested the harnesses by pulling on the straps; they seemed fine. He made some tea and sat down by the window and watched the sun go down. Too late to go today, he thought as he continued to stare out the window, watching the dusk turn into darkness. "Might as well unpack the sleigh," he said aloud, then proceeded to do so. He tried to start the machine with each trip to the sleigh, and just when he thought that it was going to start it would falter and stop.

When he finished unpacking the sleigh, he opened a can of pork and beans and ate them cold from the can. He sat down near the window again and watched the shadow of the machine taunting him every time the full moon peeked through the scattering of clouds. The dogs would howl in unison every once in a while. Hope those dogs can pull the sleigh, he thought. Don't want to have to shoot them all. He finished what was left of his tea and crawled into his bed, clothes and all.

Putta, putta, putta. The sound of the snow machine woke him from his sleep. He got up and went to the window and looked out. "Damn thing is even haunting me in my dreams," he said aloud as he watched the haunting shadow of the machine sitting there in the snow, as quiet as a mouse. He turned and went back to bed and listened to the dogs howling in the shed. The sound lulled him back to sleep.

Putta, putta, putta. The machine was running again, but this time it was chasing him. The headlight had turned into a big red evil-looking eye, and the skis had become giant talons reaching out trying to grab Skeeptoe. It was chasing him through the snow. Putta, putta, cough, chug. When Skeeptoe woke up the cabin was cold, but he was covered in sweat. He got up, started a fire in the stove and put the kettle on. Can't sleep. May as well have some tea, he thought. When the water in the kettle was boiled he made his tea, following the same ritual as before.

He sat near the window in the darkness and watched the machine sitting eerily in the shadows of the sporadic moonlight. It made him angry, the damn machine just sitting there not wanting to start but haunting him in his sleep. He turned from the window and searched for the light switch. There was only one switch, so it wasn't hard to find. He pushed the button up and the room filled with light. Sunshine in a glass, he thought.

He sat down at the table just to be away from the window and began to contemplate his life. What things would he leave behind, and to whom would he leave them upon his death? Goocho, being his best friend, would get most of his stuff. His son had no need for rifles, shotguns or traps anyway. Skeeptoe got up and grabbed the twelve-gauge shotgun he had bought last summer. He did so admire the newness of the gun. The barrel was still blue and the stock still had the fine shine all new guns had. He smiled, looked around and picked up two slugs that were sitting on the table.

He stepped out of the cabin into the cold night air carrying the shotgun. He walked over to the machine and, leaning the gun up against it, he straddled the seat. He pulled out the choke and the starting cord; the machine sputtered and then whined as the engine picked up speed. Skeeptoe let the throttle go; the machine continued to run on its own. He sat there feeling the vibration of the machine under him. He smiled slyly, then got off the machine and picked up the gun.

He loaded a slug into the chamber of the gun and aimed the gun at the machine. He pulled the trigger. The recoil of the big gun almost took him off his feet. He looked at the machine. There was a gigantic hole where the slug had hit, but the machine just kept on running. Putta, putta, putta. He reloaded the shotgun, and this time he steadied himself and took true aim. He pulled the trigger and the gun roared. Skeeptoe could almost see the slug hit as the machine exploded into a ball of flames. Must have hit the gas tank, he thought. Skeeptoe's eyes grew wider and wider as the burning machine began to move towards him. He stood frozen as the machine chugged towards him, and then he felt a hand pull him out of the path of the machine. It was Goocho. He had been awakened by the first shotgun blast.

"Shot it, eh?" Goocho said.

"Yep," replied Skeeptoe, smiling as he and Goocho stood and watched the burning machine chug and sputter and finally come to a dead stop. "Tea?" Skeeptoe asked Goocho as they turned away from the burning machine and disappeared into Skeeptoe's cabin.

Responding Personally

1. What moments do you find humorous in this story? Share your responses with a classmate.
2. Did the protagonist overreact to his frustrations or did he do the right thing at the end? Explain your opinion.

Responding Critically

3. For small group discussion: Why does Skeeptoe shoot the snowmobile? What was his motivation? How does this decision relate to his changing priorities? Would Skeeptoe feel happy at the end of the story or would he regret shooting the machine? Prepare answers to these questions and report them to the class.
4. In your opinion, what does the story reveal about the character of Skeeptoe? Another important character is his friend. How is he a confidant?
5. How does the author build suspense and create foreshadowing in the story? Present your ideas in a paragraph.
6. From which point of view is the story told? Why is that point of view effective?

Responding Creatively

7. Write an obituary for the snowmobile which Skeeptoe later places in the community newspaper.
8. Draw a four-frame cartoon for one of the scenes in the story.

Problem-Solving/Decision-Making

9. As a friend of Skeeptoe, convince him to save the machine and have it repaired. Role-play your argument for the class.

"Teach your grandmother to suck eggs," growled the old man.

Doris Lessing
Flight

Above the old man's head was the dovecote, a tall wire-netted shelf on stilts, full of strutting, preening birds. The sunlight broke on their gray breasts into small rainbows. His ears were lulled by their crooning, his hands stretched up towards his favorite, a homing pigeon, a young plump-bodied bird which stood still when it saw him and cocked a shrewd bright eye.

"Pretty, pretty, pretty," he said, as he grasped the bird and drew it down, feeling the cold coral claws tighten around his finger. Content, he rested the bird lightly on his chest, and leaned against a tree, gazing out beyond the dovecote into the landscape of a late afternoon. In folds and hollows of sunlight and shade, the dark red soil, which was broken into great dusty clods, stretched wide to a tall horizon. Trees marked the course of the valley; a stream of rich green grass the road.

His eyes travelled homewards along this road until he saw his granddaughter swinging on the gate underneath a frangipani tree. Her hair fell down her back in a wave of sunlight, and her long bare legs repeated the angles of the frangipani stems, bare, shining-brown stems among patterns of pale blossoms.

She was gazing past the pink flowers, past the railway cottage where they lived, along the road to the village.

His mood shifted. He deliberately held out his wrist for the bird to take flight, and caught it again at the moment it spread its wings. He felt the plump shape strive and strain under his fingers; and, in a sudden access of troubled spite, shut the bird into a small box and fastened the bolt. "Now you stay there," he muttered; and turned his back on the shelf of birds. He moved warily along the hedge, stalking his granddaughter, who was now looped over the gate, her head loose on her arms, singing. The light happy sound mingled with the crooning of the birds, and his anger mounted.

"Hey!" he shouted; saw her jump, look back, and abandon the gate. Her eyes veiled themselves, and she said in a pert neutral voice: "Hullo, Grandad." Politely she moved towards him, after a lingering backward glance at the road.

"Waiting for Steven, hey?" he said, his fingers curling like claws into his palm.

"Any objection?" she asked lightly, refusing to look at him.

He confronted her, his eyes narrowed, shoulders hunched, tight in a hard knot of pain which included the preening birds, the sunlight, the flowers. He said: "Think you're old enough to go courting, hey?"

The girl tossed her head at the old-fashioned phrase and sulked, "Oh, Grandad!"

"Think you want to leave home, hey? Think you can go running around the fields at night?"

Her smile made him see her, as he had every evening of this warm end-of-summer month, swinging hand in hand along the road to the village with that red-handed, red-throated, violent-bodied youth, the son of the postmaster. Misery went to his head and he shouted angrily: "I'll tell your mother!"

"Tell away!" she said, laughing, and went back to the gate.

He heard her singing, for him to hear:

"I've got you under my skin,
I've got you deep in the heart of ..."

"Rubbish," he shouted. "Rubbish. Impudent little bit of rubbish!"

Growling under his breath he turned towards the dovecote, which was his refuge from the house he shared with his daughter and her husband and their children. But now the house would be empty. Gone all the young girls with their laughter and their squabbling and their teasing. He would be left, uncherished and alone, with that square-fronted, calm-eyed woman, his daughter.

He stooped, muttering, before the dovecote, resenting the absorbed cooing birds.

From the gate the girl shouted: "Go and tell! Go on, what are you waiting for?"

Obstinately he made his way to the house, with quick, pathetic persistent glances of appeal back at her. But she never looked around. Her defiant but anxious young body stung him into love and repentance. He stopped. "But I never meant …" he muttered, waiting for her to turn and run to him. "I didn't mean …"

She did not turn. She had forgotten him. Along the road came the young man Steven, with something in his hand. A present for her? The old man stiffened as he watched the gate swing back, and the couple embrace. In the brittle shadows of the frangipani tree his granddaughter, his darling, lay in the arms of the postmaster's son, and her hair flowed back over his shoulder.

"I see you!" shouted the old man spitefully. They did not move. He stumped into the little whitewashed house, hearing the wooden veranda creak angrily under his feet. His daughter was sewing in the front room, threading a needle held to the light.

He stopped again, looking back into the garden. The couple were now sauntering among the bushes, laughing. As he watched he saw the girl escape from the youth with a sudden mischievous movement, and run off through the flowers with him in pursuit. He heard shouts, laughter, a scream, silence.

"But it's not like that at all," he muttered miserably. "It's not like that. Why can't you see? Running and giggling, and kissing and kissing. You'll come to something quite different."

He looked at his daughter with sardonic hatred, hating himself. They were caught and finished, both of them, but the girl was still running free.

"Can't you *see*?" he demanded of his invisible granddaughter, who was at that moment lying in the thick green grass with the postmaster's son.

His daughter looked at him and her eyebrows went up in tired forbearance.

"Put your birds to bed?" she asked, humoring him.

"Lucy," he said urgently. "Lucy ..."

"Well, what is it now?"

"She's in the garden with Steven."

"Now you just sit down and have your tea."

He stumped his feet alternatively, thump, thump, on the hollow wooden floor and shouted: "She'll marry him. I'm telling you, she'll be marrying him next!"

His daughter rose swiftly, brought him a cup, set him a plate.

"I don't want any tea. I don't want it, I tell you."

"Now, now," she crooned. "What's wrong with it? Why not?"

"She's eighteen. Eighteen!"

"I was married at seventeen and I never regretted it."

"Liar," he said. "Liar. Then you should regret it. Why do you make your girls marry? It's you who do it. What do you do it for? Why?"

"The other three have done fine. They've three fine husbands. Why not Alice?"

"She's the last," he mourned. "Can't we keep her a bit longer?"

"Come, now, Dad. She'll be down the road, that's all. She'll be here every day to see you."

"But it's not the same." He thought of the other three girls, transformed inside a few months from charming petulant spoiled children into serious young matrons.

"You never did like it when we married," she said. "Why not? Every time, it's the same. When I got married you made me feel like it was something wrong. And my girls the same. You get them all crying and miserable the way you go on. Leave Alice alone. She's happy." She sighed, letting her eyes linger on the sunlit garden. "She'll marry next month. There's no reason to wait."

"You've said they can marry?" he said incredulously.

"Yes, Dad, why not?" she said coldly, and took up her sewing.

His eyes stung, and he went out on the veranda. Wet spread down over his chin and he took out a handkerchief and mopped his whole face. The garden was empty.

From around the corner came the young couple; but their faces were no longer set against him. On the wrist of the postmaster's son balanced a young pigeon, the light gleaming on its breast.

"For me?" said the old man, letting the drops shake off his chin. "For me?"

"Do you like it?" The girl grabbed his hand and swung on it. "It's for you, Grandad. Steven brought it for you." They hung about him, affectionate, concerned, trying to charm away his wet eyes and his misery. They took his arms and directed him to the shelf of birds, one on each side, enclosing him, petting him, saying wordlessly that nothing would be changed, nothing could change, and that they would be with him always. The bird was proof of it, they said, from their lying happy eyes, as they thrust it on him. "There, Grandad, it's yours. It's for you."

They watched him as he held it on his wrist, stroking its soft, sun-warmed back, watching the wings lift and balance.

"You must shut it up for a bit," said the girl intimately. "Until it knows this is its home."

"Teach your grandmother to suck eggs," growled the old man.

Released by his half-deliberate anger, they fell back, laughing at him. "We're glad you like it." They moved off, now serious and full of purpose, to the gate, where they hung, backs to him, talking quietly. More than anything could, their grown-up seriousness shut him out, making him alone; also, it quietened him, took the sting out of their tumbling like puppies on the grass. They had forgotten him again. Well, so they should, the old man reassured himself, feeling his throat clotted with tears, his lips trembling. He held the new bird to his face, for the caress of its silken feathers. Then he shut it in a box and took out his favorite.

"*Now* you can go," he said aloud. He held it poised, ready for flight, while he looked down the garden towards the boy and the girl. Then, clenched in the pain of loss, he lifted the bird on his wrist, and watched it soar. A whir, and a spatter of wings, and a cloud of birds rose into the evening from the dovecote.

At the gate Alica and Steven forgot their talk and watched the birds.

On the veranda, that woman, his daughter, stood gazing, her eyes shaded with a hand that still held her sewing.

It seemed to the old man that the whole afternoon had stilled to watch his gesture of self-command, that even the leaves of the trees had stopped shaking.

Dry-eyed and calm, he let his hands fall to his sides and stood erect, staring up into the sky.

The cloud of shining silver birds flew up and up, with a shrill cleaving of wings, over the dark ploughed land and the darker belts of trees and the bright folds of grass, until they floated high in the sunlight, like a cloud of motes of dust.

They wheeled in a wide circle, tilting their wings so there was flash after flash of light, and one after another they dropped from the sunshine of the upper sky to shadow, one after another, returning to the shadowed earth over trees and grass and field, returning to the valley and the shelter of night.

The garden was all a fluster and a flurry of returning birds. Then silence, and the sky was empty.

The old man turned, slowly, taking his time; he lifted his eyes to smile proudly down the garden at his granddaughter. She was staring at him. She did not smile. She was wide-eyed, and pale in the cold shadow, and he saw the tears run shivering off her face.

Responding Personally

1. How does the atmosphere change as the story unfolds? Do you feel happy or sad for the grandfather at the end of the story?
2. Write about a close relationship you have had or would like to have had with a grandparent.

Responding Critically

3. With a partner, discuss the goal of the grandfather. In your opinion, does he fail or succeed in the pursuit of his goal? Why?

4. Are the grandfather's fear and objections understandable and justified, or is he simply a meddlesome old man? Explain, using evidence from the story.
5. For paragraph response: Write your ideas about what the birds symbolize and interpret the meaning of the story's title. (You might want to brainstorm ideas with a partner first.)
6. For discussion: Analyze the irony of each of the following:
   a) The grandfather's thoughts as he looks at his daughter, "They were caught and finished, both of them, but the girl was still running free" (page 171)
   b) The emotional reactions of the old man and his granddaughter in the concluding paragraph (page 174).

Responding Creatively

7. Write a postcard from the granddaughter that comes to the grandfather a month later, thanking him for his concerns and choice.
8. Find a song, poem, or rock video clip on the topic of saying goodbye or "letting go." Share it with the class and tell how your choice relates to the story.

Problem-Solving/Decision-Making

9. Recall a moment when you had to "let go" of someone or something precious to you. Explain how you felt at the time and how things finally turned out. Write your experience in a journal response.

SP 0:02:01
SP 0:02:01
SP 0:02:01
SP 0:02:01
SP 0:02:01
SP 0:02:01

UNIT SEVEN

Theme and Meaning

Why do readers and listeners find stories so appealing? If you were asked that question, you might answer that stories are entertaining. This is true: for centuries, human beings have enjoyed being drawn into the lively, interesting, curious world of literature.

Many people can recall childhood stories that caused them to respond in ways such as worrying about the fate of fairy tale characters, becoming upset at the thoughts of ogres and scary creatures hiding under bridges, or cheering when the evil wolves were finally defeated. As children grow older, they usually become more interested in mystery stories that need unravelling, super heroes that fight against seemingly impossible odds, or young people like themselves who are fighting different forms of injustice. As they become adults, even though their tastes in reading will likely change yet again, they will still always love a good entertaining story.

Short stories offer more than entertainment, however. Many short stories provide insights into what our world is like and why human beings behave as they do. These insights or truths about human nature and our society are the themes of stories included in this unit.

The three selections that follow offer insights or truths for readers to consider. The first story, "A Television Drama," describes how an ordinary day is disrupted for an urban housewife when she realizes the reality of a violent crime that is being reported on the radio station she is listening to. The second story, "The Whale," provides a humorous love story with an unexpected ending that provides the reader with different ways of looking at a universal theme. The third story, "The Empty Frame," tells the story of an insane artist who offers his thoughts and feelings about life to anyone who will listen, and becomes so convincing that others begin to believe his ideas.

Carolee wanted to help him, whoever he was.

Jane Rule
A Television Drama

At one-thirty in the afternoon, Carolee Mitchell was running the vacuum cleaner, or she would have heard the first sirens and looked out. After the first, there weren't any others. The calling voices, even the number of dogs barking, could have been students on their way back to school, high-spirited in the bright, cold earliness of the year. Thinking back on the sounds, Carolee remembered a number of car doors being slammed, that swallow of air and report which made her smooth her hair automatically even if she wasn't expecting anyone. But what caught her eye finally was what always caught her eye: the flight of a bird from a treetop in the ravine out over the fringe of trees at the bottom of her steeply sloping front lawn, nearly private in the summer, exposed now to the startling activity of the street.

Three police cars were parked in front of the house, a motorcycle like a slanted stress in the middle of the intersection, half a dozen more police cars scattered up and down the two blocks. There were men in uniform up on her neighbor's terrace with rifles and field glasses. Police with dogs were crossing the empty field at the bottom of the ravine. More cars were arriving, police and reporters with cameras and sound equipment. Mingling among the uniforms and equipment were the neighbors: Mrs. Rolston from the house across the street who had obviously not taken time to put on a coat and was rubbing her arms absent-mindedly as she stood and talked. Jane Carey from next door with a scarf tied round her head and what looked like one of her son's jackets thrown over her shoulders, old Mr. Monkson, a few small children. Cars and people kept arriving. Suddenly there was a voice magnified to reach even Carolee, surprised and unbelieving behind her picture window.

"Clear the street. All householders return to or stay in your houses. Clear the street."

Mrs. Rolston considered the idea for a moment but did not go in. The others paid no attention at all. Carolee wondered if she should go out just to find out what on earth was going on. Perhaps she should telephone someone, but everyone she might phone was already in the street. Was it a gas main? Not with all those dogs. A murder? It seemed unlikely that anyone would kill anyone else on this street, where every child had his own bedroom and most men either studies or basement workshops to retreat into. In any case, it was the middle of the afternoon. Mrs. Cole had come out on her balcony with field glasses focussed on the place where the dogs and police had entered the ravine. Field glasses. Where were Pete's field glasses? Carolee thought she knew, but she did not move to get them. She would not know what she was looking for in the undergrowth or the gardens.

"Clear the street. All householders return to or stay in your houses."

Police radios were now competing with each other. "Suspect last apprehended in the alley between ..." "House to house search ..." "Ambulance ..."

If one of those policemen standing about on the street would come to search the house, Carolee could at least find out what was going on. Was that a TV crew? Dogs were barking in the ravine. Did police dogs bark? Nobody on the street seemed to be doing anything, except for the motorcycle policeman who was turning away some cars. Maybe Carolee should go empty the dishwasher and then come back. It was pointless to stand here by the window. Nothing was happening, or, if something was happening, Carolee couldn't see the point of it. She went to the window in Pete's study to see if she could discover activity on the side street. There were more policeman, and far up the block an ambulance was pulling away without a siren, its red light slowly circling. Carolee watched it until it turned the corner at the top of the hill. Then she turned back toward the sound of barking dogs and radios, but paused as she turned.

There, sitting against the curve of the laurel hedge by the lily pond, was a man, quite a young man, his head down, his left hand against his right shoulder. He was sick or hurt or dead. Or not really there at all, something Carolee's imagination had put there to explain the activity in the street, part of a collage, like an unlikely photograph in the middle of a painting. But he raised his head slightly then, and Carolee saw the blood on his jacket and trousers.

"I must call the police," she said aloud, but how could she call the police when they were already there, three of them standing not seventy feet away, just below the trees on the parking strip? She must call someone, but all the neighbors were still out of doors. And what if the police did discover him? He might be shot instead of helped. Carolee wanted to help him, whoever he was. It was such an odd way he was sitting, his legs stretched out in front of him so that he couldn't possibly have moved quickly. He might not be able to move at all. But she couldn't get to him, not without being seen. Suddenly he got to his feet, his left hand still against his right shoulder and also holding the lower part of his ducked face. He walked to the end of the curve of hedge as if it was very difficult for him to move, and then he began a stumbling run across the front lawn, through the trees, and out onto the parking strip. There he turned, hesitated, and fell on his back. Carolee had heard no shot. Now her view was blocked by a gathering of police and reporters, drawn to that new center like leaves to a central drain.

"Suspect apprehended on ..."

What had he done? What had that hurt and stumbling boy done? Carolee was standing with her hand on the transistor radio before it occurred to her to turn it on.

"We interrupt this program with a news bulletin. A suspect has been apprehended on ..."

He had robbed a bank, run a car into a tree, shot a policeman, been shot at.

"And now, here is our reporter on the scene."

Carolee could see the reporter quite clearly, standing in the street in front of the house, but she could hear only the radio voice, explaining what had happened.

"And now the ambulance is arriving ..." as indeed it was. "The suspect, suffering from at least three wounds, who seems near death, is being lifted onto a stretcher ..." This she couldn't see. It seemed to take a very long time before police cleared a path for the ambulance, again silent, its red light circling, to move slowly down the block and out of sight.

A newspaper reporter was walking up the front path, but Carolee didn't answer the door. She stood quietly away from the window and waited until he was gone. Then she went to the kitchen and began to empty the dishwasher. It was two o'clock. She turned on the radio again to listen to the regular news report. The details were the same. At three o'clock the hospital had reported that the policeman was in the operating room having a bullet removed from his right lung. At four o'clock the suspect was reported in only fair condition from wounds in the shoulder, jaw, leg and hand.

At five o'clock Pete came home, the evening paper in his hand. "Well, you've had quite a day," he said. "Are you all right?"

"Yes," Carolee said, her hands against his cold jacket, her cheek against his cold face. "Yes, I'm all right. What did the paper say?"

"It's all diagrams," he said, holding out the front page to her.

There was a map of the whole neighborhood, a sketched aerial map, a view of the roof of their house Carolee had never had. She followed the dots and arrows to the hood of a car crumpled under a flower of foliage, on again across the ravine, up their side hill, and there was the laurel hedge and the jelly bean lily pond, but the dots didn't stop there, arced round rather and immediately down through the trees to a fallen doll, all alone, not a policeman or reporter in sight, lying there exposed to nothing but a God's-eye view.

"You must have seen him," Pete said.

"Yes," Carolee agreed, still looking down on the rooftops of all her neighbors' houses."

"Did it frighten you?" Pete asked.

"Not exactly. It was hard to believe, and everything seemed to happen so very slowly."

"Did you get a good look at him?"

"I guess not really," Carolee said. Had he sat there by the laurel hedge at all, his long, stiff legs stretched out in front of him? The map didn't show it.

"Something has got to be done about all this violence," Pete said.

His tone and the look on his face made Carolee realize that Pete has been frightened, much more frightened than she was. Those dotted lines across his front lawn, that figure alone in the landscape—Carolee felt herself shaken by a new fear, looking at what Pete had seen.

"I'll get us a drink," Pete said.

Once they sat down, Carolee tried to tell her husband what it had been like, all those women just standing out in the street. She told him about the guns and field glasses and dogs and cameras. She did not tell him about the man, hurt, by the laurel hedge.

Pete turned on the television, and they watched three minutes of fast-moving images, first the policeman lifted into an ambulance, then officers and dogs running through the field, finally glimpses of the suspect on the ground and then shifted onto a stretcher; and, while they watched, a voice told them of the robbery, the chase, the capture. Finally several people were quickly interviewed, saying such things as, "I saw him go over the fence" or "He fell practically at my feet." That was Mrs. Rolston, still rubbing her cold arms in the winter day.

"I'm glad you had the good sense to stay inside," Pete said. He was holding her hand, beginning to relax into indignation and relief.

Carolee wasn't there, nor was the man there. If she had spoken to that reporter, if she had said then, "I saw him. He was sitting by the laurel hedge," would the dots in the paper have changed? Would the cameras have climbed into their nearly exposed winter garden? Would she believe now what she couldn't quite believe even then, that she stood at that window and saw a man dying in her garden?

Now a labor union boss was talking, explaining the unfair practices of the compensation board. Nearly at once, young marines were running, firing, falling. Planes were dropping bombs. Carolee wasn't there, but it seemed real to her, terribly real, so that for a moment she forgot Pete's hand in hers, her safe house on a safe street, and was afraid.

Responding Personally

1. Describe how you might have reacted if you were in the same situation as Carolee.
2. With a classmate, consider the impact of violence on people in real life and how the media contributes to that impact.

Responding Critically

3. For paragraph response: What epiphany does Carolee have at the end of the story? Is she a static or dynamic character? Justify your choice with details from the story.
4. How does Pete's reactions to the events differ from Carolee's? What might be the reason for the difference?
5. In a group, consider how the following details add to the story's impact:
   a) "It seemed unlikely that anyone would kill anyone else on this street, where every child had his own bedroom and most men either studies or basement workshops to retreat into."
   b) "… A fallen doll, all alone, not a policeman or reporter in sight, lying there exposed to nothing but a God's-eye view."
   c) "Pete turned on the television, and they watched three minutes of fast-moving images.… Finally several people were quickly interviewed."
6. What was the media coverage like for this event? Was it realistic or sensational? Record your viewpoint. Does the way in which the media report events such as this one affect the response of viewers, listeners, and/or readers? Share your opinions in a group.

Responding Creatively

7. In poetic form, describe the images that enter into a nightmare Carolee might have later that night.
8. With a partner, improvise an interview between Carolee and a television reporter.

Problem-Solving/Decision-Making

9. Near the end of the story, Pete says, "Something has got to be done about all this violence." Do you agree that something should be done to make people feel safer in their homes? If so, what strategies would your suggest? Write your recommendations in a letter to the local police department.

"Call me a liar," he said with dignity, "it doesn't bother me."

Yves Thériault

The Whale

Translated by Patricia Sillers

On every boat and quay from Gaspé to Paspébiac the news spread like wildfire: Ambroise Bourdages claimed that—singlehandedly—he had landed a whale!

The fishermen were all getting a great kick out of it. Now if Ambroise had claimed that he had caught a two-hundred pound cod that had later managed to get free of the hook, everyone would have made a solemn show of believing it. That would have been an admissible exaggeration, quite in keeping with local instincts, habits, and customs ... But a whale?

Stretching his arms wide Ambroise insisted: "I'm telling you, a whale! Colossal! As big as a boat—bigger even! Ahhh, my friends, my friends ... I spot it sunning itself. Quick as I can I grab a rope, I get a hook on it, I bait it with a herring, I attach a floater, and then I let it out behind the boat ... the whale spies the bait and starts making for it. I let out the line ... a hundred, two hundred feet. The whale swallows the bait—and it's hooked!"

"This hook of yours, how big is it?" asked Vilmont Babin.

"A big cod hook. Maybe an inch and a half ..."

"And it hooked the whale?"

"Yes."

A tremendous burst of laughter shook the whole quay.

About a dozen fishermen were listening as Ambroise related his adventure. A few girls were there too, as there always are when the boats come in. Among them was Gabrielle, who smiled too much at Adélard these days—at least in the opinion of Ambroise, who had eyes only for her.

Unlike the others, who found his story too good—and too funny—to be true, she listened gravely and did not laugh.

There was a look in Gabrielle's eyes that Ambroise could not quite make out. It was a serious expression that suited her natural reserve and good manners—manners very different from those of the rude, obnoxious Adélard.

He was there too, laughing with the others at Ambroise, making fun of him.

"Did you stow your whale in the hold?" he asked Ambroise. "Or weren't you strong enough to haul such a big trophy into your boat?"

This produced a great roar of laughter. Everyone wanted to slap Adélard on the back. Here was a match for Ambroise! Someone with the answer to a tall tale!

"Call me a liar," he said with dignity, "it doesn't bother me. Just remember this: if I were on my deathbed and my mother asked me to repeat every word I've just told you, I'd do it. I didn't lie to you. My men were asleep below. We were heading out towards the Shippegan banks and I was at the tiller. I landed a whale … and anyone who doesn't believe me can forget it. I know what I did. I hooked a whale with a cod-hook."

He spat on the timbers of the quay, turned on his heel, and left.

Naturally it wasn't long before they were talking about Ambroise Bourdages's alleged miraculous catch in every village on the Coast. As it made the rounds from one quay to another the story was altered and embellished out of all recognition. Ambroise was floored by the version that got back to him.

It was Clovis, the prissy, affected son of the banker in Port-Savoie, where Ambroise lived, who brought back the first of this bizarre gossip.

"Do you know what they're saying at Paspébiac?" he asked Ambroise. "My poor friend, you'd never believe it! It's really terrible!"

"What are they saying?"

"I said it's terrible, but to tell the truth it's mostly funny."

"Let's say it *is* funny. What is it?"

"Good heavens you're tiresome! So impatient ... Well, to hear them talk it seems you caught a whale with your bare hands, held on to it for dear life all by yourself, fought like the devil to haul it by the tail into your boat, and in the end it got away."

Ambroise groaned.

"Ah, no, no! They're all making fun of me!"

Just at that moment Gabrielle came out of the Company store. Her hair floated on the breeze and her smile was as bright as a sunflower.

"How beautiful she is," thought Ambroise, "so tall and graceful. If only she could like me!"

But as she passed close by Ambroise she gave a sarcastic little laugh.

"I have to get proof of my story!" cried Ambroise, when Gabrielle was out of earshot. "Clovis, no one would ever take you for a liar! A banker's son isn't allowed to tell lies!"

"Of course I mustn't tell lies. Lying isn't nice. Besides, I wouldn't want to disgrace my father."

"All right then! Tomorrow you and I are going out to sea. You'll be my witness. We're going to catch another whale, and this time it won't get away!"

Next day they headed out on the water. Despite the sunshine the seas were heavy and sullen. The boat rolled and pitched for seven long miles. But then, just at the end of the run, they saw a jet of spray rising from a whale that was frolicking in the waves—not six yards from the boat.

To summarize the day's adventures we'll say that Ambroise, using all his fisherman's skill, managed to catch the whale with his cod-hook. This was not easily done. The sea monster gave a magnificent display of its strength and agility. On three different occasions, while driving furiously in an effort to get free of the hook, the whale almost capsized the boat. Finally exhausted, it rose calmly to the surface. Ambroise fastened the rope and took the tiller. Slowly he towed his trophy towards the moorings of Port-Savoie.

He was bursting with joy. It had been accomplished despite all the doubt and sarcasm. Even Gabrielle would have to agree that he, Ambroise Bourdages, had not lied about capturing a whale. In fact it was so far from being a lie that a week later he had gone out and caught another.

This was the way to silence the scandalmongers.

At the same time it ought to establish him as the greatest fisherman and the most respected man on the Coast.

It is not every day that a man catches a whale with such simple tackle. And even if there is an element of luck in it, there is also an element of know-how and gumption that cannot be overlooked.

But just as they were about a mile from Port-Savoie the whale suddenly came to life. With one powerful sneeze it spat out the hook—as if to show that it had only been toying with them and could quite easily have escaped earlier, if it had wanted to.

Then it dived and disappeared under the water.

This loss, however, did not bother Ambroise too much.

He had a witness with him. An honest man, a banker's son, a person to corroborate his story who would be believed without question.

As he jumped up onto the quay he let out a great cry.

"Ahoy!"

About fifty people, all aware of the expedition, were waiting when Ambroise and Clovis returned.

Even Gabrielle was there.

Ambroise quickly told what had happened. He described everything in detail. And as the ripples of laughter began to spread: "Listen Ambroise," and Vilmont Babin, "you can get away with it once, but the same lie twice—it won't work!"

With a great sweep of his arm Ambroise pointed to Clovis.

"Clovis was there. He's my witness. An honest witness. He saw it all. He'll tell you that the whale got away just about a mile from here."

But Clovis was sporting a smile that looked more like a grin. Then, in his piping voice he declared: "Ambroise is a liar. I never saw him catch a whale!"

The shouts and threats that followed this declaration were so clamorous, and poor Ambroise was so crushed by Clovis's double-dealing, that all he could think of was to run away as fast as possible.

Two hours later he risked going outside again. Clovis was standing by the Post Office. Ambroise hurried over to him. The young man waited for him imperturbably.

"Snake in the grass!" Ambroise yelled at him. "Liar! Worse—you're a perjurer! I'll have you arrested!"

"Just a minute, my friend," said Clovis stiffly. "There's something you don't know. I have my eye on Gabrielle too. Do you really think I'm going to let you impress her with your whale-fishing story? I've decided to fight—with my own weapons! The fortunes of war, old fellow, I'm sorry."

But Ambroise, disconsolate, had already left. He felt trapped, beaten. Farewell dreams! He'd lost Gabrielle forever to wilier men. Clovis, for one. And Adélard. While he, Ambroise, was fighting shadows.

Once again he raced for home.

But as he was entering the house the sun suddenly reappeared and joy began to revive his hopes. Gabrielle was there, in the kitchen, with Ambroise's mother.

"Ah!" said Ambroise … "Gabrielle?"

She smiled at him.

"Ambroise, I apologise. Forgive me … I misunderstood your lie about the whale!"

"But," said Ambroise, "it wasn't a …"

Gabrielle waved aside his explanation.

"When you tried to tell your story for the second time today, I admit I was disgusted. I knew you were trying to impress me. But after I got home I began to think about it. Do you know what I decided, Ambroise?"

"No ... no."

"It's a lucky girl that has a fellow who'll go against everyone just for her, simply to impress her, to win her ..."

Ambroise was about to protest strongly again, but suddenly he thought better of it. A sly gleam appeared in his eye. So this was the way the land lay? Well, then.

"Gabrielle," he said softly, "it was the least I could do. A lie like that about a cod would never have been enough—not grand enough! But a whale, an impossible catch ... It was a matter of gallantry, of giving it enough weight—you know?"

"Of course. That's why I'm here ..."

So Ambroise took her by the hand and led her out into the village and walked with her so that everyone would plainly see that in spite of everything he'd made the best catch of his life ... and to hell with the whale!

Responding Personally

1. Describe to a partner a favourite love story (or adventure story) and explain why you like it.
2. Recall a time when your real intentions in a situation were greatly misunderstood. Share your experience with a classmate.

Responding Critically

3. This story might be described as a series of events, each of which turns out differently from what readers or characters expect. Describe each event, explaining its unexpected outcome.
4. With a partner, find examples of each of the three types of irony.

5. Compose a thematic statement for the story. Compare it with one prepared by a classmate.
6. What does the story reveal about the community in which it was set? Refer to details in the story to support your answer.

Responding Creatively

7. Prepare an illustrated brochure on different ways to win someone else's attention and affection.
8. With a classmate, role-play a scene in which Ambroise tells the townsfolk about his impending engagement.

Problem-Solving/Decision-Making

9. What are some ways in which people can become more credible in their dealings with others and thereby raise other people's opinions of them? How does one become an authoritative source, or a trustworthy and respected person? In a small group, brainstorm these questions and report your conclusions to the class.

"All great people in the world have been accused of insanity!"

Khalil Bawar
The Empty Frame

Translated by Ali Kumail Qizalbash and Asif Farrukhi

He did not look like a madman at all. Tall, well-built, a well-proportioned nose, eyes with a lot of depth, and curved, artistic fingers. His face reflected the depth of his thoughts. Whenever he looked at anybody he looked with the depths of his being, as if he had reached a new and wondrous world. Now everybody had started seeing signs of insanity in whatever he did. They all ridiculed and poked fun at him. A short while ago, one of his friends had remarked in a tone which showed more sarcasm than concern: "He is an excellent artist but he has lost his sanity!"

He was used to hearing such comments every day. But today this rather casual remark from his friend lay like a heavy burden on him. It became so unbearably heavy that his face began to change colour and beads of perspiration began to pour down his face like rainwater on a well-watered piece of land. He loudly proclaimed to his friend:

"It is you who have lost your sanity—all of you—you pay no attention to what I am saying and neither do you leave me alone to do what I like."

The doctor signalled his friends to leave. When only the two of them were left in the room, the doctor asked him sympathetically: "Why do these people think that you are mad?"

"All great people in the world have been accused of insanity!" pat came his unabashed reply.

The doctor was astonished and gave his face a searching look, then rephrased his question carefully: "All right, what you are saying is correct. But why do people say such things about you?"

He was looking at the charts hanging on the walls of his consulting clinic.

"People say the same kind of things about me as they used to say about Socrates, Newton, and Galileo."

He turned his weary eyes towards the doctor and began to speak about those eminent persons who had the power to express the secrets of life openly.

"Socrates regarded life as based on ideas and thoughts, and Galileo realized that the earth is round and revolves around the sun. These were truths but people were not ready to accept them. Just as when I tell them that I have created a picture which changes from moment to moment and has a different look each time, they refuse to accept this. But it doesn't matter ..."

He quickly got up from his chair and began looking at the wall charts which showed the different parts of the brain.

For doctors, each person is a living museum, but sometimes they are confronted with patients whose questions humble them, and this was such a patient. The doctor too got up from his chair and tried to convert his question into an answer.

"This means that you have made such a picture ..."

"Not made but created," he cut the doctor short. "There is a world of difference between the two words, making and creating, if anybody tries to understand."

"All right, I get it." The doctor immediately agreed with him. "So you have created a picture which looks completely real?"

"Not 'looks real,' it is real. If you don't believe me, then come with me and take a look."

He caught hold of the doctor's hands and began to pull him along. "Come, sir, come!"

"If you wish. If you have really created something, then I will definitely come along with you and look at your work. But tell me, whose picture is it? It must be the picture of a very pretty girl."

He shook his head. "No, not at all. It is not the picture of a girl. It is the picture of this land on which you and I and all of us live."

"A picture of this land?" The doctor's curiosity was aroused. It seemed to be a strange case and his mind was full of new questions. "Picture? A picture of the land? A picture changing from moment to moment?"

"Yes. I have imagined this land of ours and created a picture. But it's a pity that what was imagined has moved away from the reality." He started shaking his head and putting it in his hands as if it was under a heavy load. He kept on talking. "When I created this painting, I liked it very much and I hung it in my room."

It was the doctor's habit that he could fall back on his book learning and refer back to cases in his memory. He would utter a monosyllable now and then to keep pace with the conversation. On the other hand, his patient was enjoying the conversation and was speaking without interruption.

"After a few days, when I came to see the picture, it was covered with snakes. I could see snakes crawling everywhere."

"Snakes? What snakes?" the doctor asked in amazement.

"Yes, snakes. I saw them with my own eyes. And everybody could see them but nobody cared to."

He was becoming agitated. He would go to one wall and then to the other. He would sit on the chair and then suddenly get up. The doctor was restlessly pacing the room also. Whenever his patient paused, he would egg him on. "So what happened then?"

"Then one day I saw the entire picture drenched in blood. All rivers were flowing with blood. The earth began to absorb blood. All the *karez,* wells, and springs began to spout blood."

The doctor could not control himself and he asked, "Could it be that when you thought that you saw the snakes, you became afraid and began to see blood everywhere?"

"I don't know. I've never thought about it," he said, and then continued as before:

"And then one night, when I returned home, I saw that my creation was destroyed. There was nothing left. The land stood devastated, with no sign of its former beauty. It was as if a whole mountain had come crashing down on me. I lay awake in this condition all night. And in the morning, when I glanced at the frame, then the world which had been destroyed the night before was visible once again. But all the trees, flowers, and leaves showed the unmistakable signs of autumn. The land was an autumn garden and yellow leaves were blown here and there by the winds. There was nothing else that I could see in the picture."

"Could it be that you were depressed that night and that is why you saw all those things in the picture?" the doctor interrupted him again.

"It is hard for me to say what my state was at that time. But I am not talking about myself. I am talking about the picture which was my creation," he said.

"But you must pay some attention to your own condition also." It sounded as if the physician was preaching to him.

"All right, doctor. If I have a problem then I will analyse myself, but now you must come with me and look at the painting so you can see if I am telling the truth or not!"

The doctor was perplexed whether to go with the patient or not. But he caught the doctor's hand and tried to pull him along. "Come on, please come. My home is very near."

Reluctantly the doctor went along. Throughout the short distance, he kept on talking, describing his creation. It seemed to the doctor that he was close to grasping the root cause of his problem.

As soon as they reached his home, he dragged the doctor to his room and pointed very excitedly. "Look for yourself!"

He pointed to an empty frame hanging on the wall.

"Look at the land! It is on fire, all of it! You wouldn't believe me, but now see for yourself how the entire land is burning. Tell me the truth, doctor! You can see the flames yourself, can't you?"

The doctor felt as if he was on the verge of the truth. He felt that he was close to the inner feelings of the creator. He spoke very softly, "This land that you can see burning, I can also feel the fire."

He heard these words and repeated them as if he couldn't believe his ears. "Really, doctor? You can also feel the fire?"

And then he began to shout, "I told you so. I was telling the truth. I am not mad … I am not mad. Those people are mad who don't believe me, who don't understand me. They deny my creation ... they are mad, all are mad, mad!"

He was standing in front of the empty frame and shouting at the top of his voice.

Responding Personally

1. For discussion: At what point, do you begin to doubt the sanity of the patient? Do you think the doctor handled the patient appropriately?
2. Describe a picture you can imagine, but have not painted.

Responding Critically

3. Is it appropriate that the story ends with the climax? What do you think the doctor sees? Compare your response with another student's.
4. In a small group, discuss the symbolic painting. What does the painting mean or signify to the patient and doctor?
5. Referring to details in the story, write a response explaining what you learned about the artist, art, imagination, and insanity.
6. In a small group, come to a consensus about a thematic statement for the story.

Responding Creatively

7. Draw three pictures of the frame's contents: one from the artist's perspective, one from the doctor's, and one from your own.
8. Write the doctor's diagnosis after his visit to the patient's residence.

Problem-Solving/Decision-Making

9. For discussion: Who has the best understanding of the value or meaning of a painting: the artist, the critic, or the ordinary viewer? Are beauty and truth merely in the eye of the beholder, or can these qualities exist independently of subjective opinion?

UNIT EIGHT

Stories for Further Reading

In the first seven units, you have seen how various fiction elements contribute to the successful development of short stories. This last unit gives you a chance to explore ways in which these stories communicate messages intended by their authors using the different fiction elements.

The first story, "Call Me," uses a specific style and format to provide a satirical view of technology in modern communication and its impact on human relationships. The next story, "Cancer," also uses effects such as the capitalized and italicized words to explore the strange life of a young woman who wants to be the centre of attention. The third story, "Aero Bars," offers a more positive approach to the topic of cancer. In this story, a mere two paragraphs capture a son's relationship with his seriously ill father. In the fourth story, "The Dress," a South American writer uses dialogue and description to present a tense conflict between a controlling mother and her grown-up daughter. "The Third or Fourth Happiest Man in Nova Scotia" introduces readers to a comical character who earnestly tends to local injured wildlife. "All the Colors of Sunset" offers a poignant character profile of an aboriginal grandmother who finally comes to grips with the death of her beloved granddaughter. In the final story of the unit, "Willow Waist," a Chinese writer explores the relationship between two elderly people who have remained intimate friends despite their separation and different lifestyles.

This has been a generic,
no-name brand message.

Judy McCrosky
Call Me

(A penthouse high above the Big City. The living room is spacious, and contains a white modular sofa with matching chairs and three glass-and-chrome tables. The room is dark and shadowed. On one table stands a telephone and an answering machine. A red light on the answering machine is on. The only other light in the room washes in from the City, through the glass double doors along the back wall. The phone rings.)

Hello. This is telephone answering machine XB 1700. I am currently on my coffee break. If you wish to speak with me, you must make an appointment. Leave a message after the tone, and I'll have my human contact you to set one up.

—Shawna, it's George. Sorry I missed your call. Listen, I have a free evening next week. Let's get together. Call me.

(A young woman enters. She wears a square-shouldered black jacket and a calf-length skirt and carries a briefcase. She places the briefcase on the floor beside the glass doors. She lifts her arms above her head and stretches, her body a dark silhouette against the shimmering lights of the City below.)

Hi. You have reached George Lipincott's line. This evening I'm at the office for a couple of hours finishing up an account, and then it's off to the ballet. Please leave a message after the beep and I'll get back to you as soon as I can.

—George. Shawna here. Sorry, next week is fully booked. I do have Thursday the 26th free. How about a movie?

Sorry, I can't come to the phone right now. I'm watching all seventy-nine episodes of Star Trek, *non-stop. Leave a message after the tone and I'll call you when I beam back to earth.*

—Ha ha, great greeting, Shawna. Love it. You Trekkie, you. It's George. The 26th sounds fine. I've marked it in my calendar, and I'll see you then. 8:30?

(The young woman is sitting on a chair. Her briefcase is open on a low table in front of her. It is early evening, and the orange and pink of a magnificent sunset can be seen through the glass doors. The young woman appears to be satisfied with the contents of the briefcase. She nods once and snaps it shut. Standing, she takes a navy blue blazer from where it lies across the sofa, puts it on, and leaves. The phone rings.)

Hello. (There are sounds of children laughing.) *As you can hear, I'm a little busy right now.* (The sounds intensify.) *Leave a message after the tone and I'll get back to you as soon as the kids untie me.*

—Hi, it's George. Just wanted to tell you how much I enjoyed the other evening. The movie was good, and sharing it with you made it special. You sitting there in the dark beside me, well, I'll only tell you I had a hard time concentrating on the movie. Your silk-clad leg, so close to mine. Our arms, brushing as they shared the arm-rest. I'd better stop right here. If I say more it might shock those kids I heard. Say, where'd those kids come from, anyway?

You have reached George Lipincott's line. I'm out all day today, no time even to come home to change before dinner tonight. John Crosbie is the speaker. Leave a message after the beep and I'll call you first thing tomorrow.

—I borrowed the kids from my sister. I enjoyed the other evening too. Sorry I had to rush off right after the movie, but the presentation the next day was a success, so I'm glad I put in those extra hours that night. Let's get together again. No movies, though. Let's go somewhere we can talk. I'd like to get to know you, George.

I can't come to the phone right now. Please leave a message after the tone and I'll get back to you as soon as I can. Thank you. This has been a generic, no-name brand message.

—Shawna, Shawna, how do you think of them? And do you think of what your last message did to me? That husky undertone in your voice when you said you want to get to know me. Well. I'll tell you, my heart rate shot up even higher than it does during my aerobics class. By all means, let's go somewhere we can talk. How about we meet for a drink on the 6th? 9:30?

(The apartment is dark. A shaft of light slides across the floor. There is the sound of a door closing. The light disappears abruptly. The young woman enters. She drops her briefcase and walks slowly across the floor. She falls into a seat and takes off her shoes. She rubs one foot. After a while she stands up and exits. The apartment is quiet. Then there is the sound of a shower running. The phone rings.)

I can't come to the phone right now. Please leave a message after the tone and I'll get back to you as soon as I can. Thank you. This has been a generic, no-name brand message.

—Shawna darling, you must be working too hard. The same greeting again on your machine? Still, I mustn't chide you. Your dedication is one of the things I admire most about you. Thank you for the other night. I've never had a watermelon daiquiri before. Dee-lish. And the band was good too. I liked watching you move to the music. In the dark your red dress shimmered enticingly and your hair was like a pale silver cloud. I liked it even better when the music turned slow and you stepped into my arms. The scent of your hair had my senses reeling. What kind of shampoo do you use? And when can I see you again?

Hi. You have reached George Lipincott's line. I've gone sailing today. George is a lucky devil, you must be thinking. Don't worry, it's business. A new client to entertain. And, lest we forget, it's deductible! Leave a message after the beep and I'll call you the moment I come in, my hair smelling of salt spray, and my eyes filled with sea and sky.

—Hi George. It's me. *(Sounds of heavy breathing.)* That's from the thought of you with your hair ruffled by the wind, smelling of the sea. I enjoyed the other night too. Dancing was fun. Still, it's a shame the music was so loud. We weren't really able to talk. And it was dark in there, wasn't it? What colour are your eyes? If they are filled with sea and sky, does that mean they're blue?

No brilliant witty scintillating greeting today. It's your turn. Leave your message after you hear the tone.

—Sorry about the mixup last night. It's George, by the way. The boss came in just as I was leaving and asked me to go through an account with him. He depends on me, I couldn't let him down. By the time I got to the restaurant, you'd left. Can you ever forgive me?

I want to tell you something funny that just happened. I was in my car driving home. I was alone. No more car pools for me. I value that time to unwind on my own from my day. Anyway, I got stopped at the 52nd and 8th traffic light, and I happened to glance at the car next to me. The driver was you! I picked up my car phone to call you. But then I didn't, I was struck by a sudden doubt. What if it wasn't really you? It's always been so dark when we've been together. Is your car a black BMW?

Sorry if this message isn't witty or scintillating enough.

(The apartment is dark. A full moon hangs in the night sky outside the glass double doors. Silver light bathes the modular sofa but the rest of the room is in heavy shadow. Off to one side, the red light of the telephone answering machine glows, a beacon in the dark.)

Responding Personally

1. With a partner, compare notes on the funniest recorded messages you have heard.

2. Is there truth to the story's portrayal of technology's impact on communication and human relationships? Explain.

Responding Critically

3. How is the story's title ironic and related to its plot?
4. What did you learn about each of the two characters and their relationship from their calls and messages? Summarize your ideas for each character and share them with a partner.
5. "Call Me" is a satire and an experimental form of short story. In your opinion, does it work as both? Why or why not?
6. For small group discussion: One of the criteria of a good story is its relevance to a modern audience. Does the story speak to audiences today? Comment.

Responding Creatively

7. With a classmate, role-play a scene in which George and Shawna actually meet in person and talk about their relationship.
8. Design a Web site for one of the characters which reflects his or her personality.

Problem-Solving/Decision-Making

9. Write a script of a live conversation between George and Shawna in which they consider how they can get their schedules to come together better.

It is not until mid-October that the lie expands.

Janice Deal
Cancer

They move outside the theatre, the lights on Michigan Avenue are soft, bleeding almost, and it is beautiful except he says, "Let's stop for coffee, a bite to eat maybe," and she feels her heart moving, she has nothing to say, the movie has disguised the lack but now surely he will find out.

The alarm rings at 6:00 A.M. and Janine is sluggish but she forces herself out of bed. Feet moving rough across the cold wooden floor, the shower hard and bright behind rippled glass. Janine is always up at 6:00, it is part of her routine, the shower/breakfast/stretching that she dutifully accomplishes each morning before she allows herself to read. Not the morning paper, round and pulp smelling, pushed against her apartment door. But fairy tales, poetry, the stuff that braces her dreamlike for another day.

The paper she will read on the bus, still partly attuned to princes, to crimson and russet gowns and glistering shoes. But she always reads the first page, always, it is her way of "staying abreast," and at night she will read one informative thing, an entry in the encyclopedia perhaps (she is through the Bs) or maybe an article in *Newsweek*.

In this manner she is busy. And she never takes her work home with her, never, and she also does not worry over the disappointments.

She will not think of last night, the long pauses over pie and coffee. "This is my favorite coffee shop," he had smiled, he had liked the movie, still thought things were going well. But she was frightened, frantically trying to recall what she had read that morning—what they could talk about. She was drawing a blank, could not remember what it was he did for a living, and finally he, too, had fallen silent. And it was a relief to be home (her home), the Monet poster on the wall and the yellow pottery jar of plastic daisies on the breakfront, and she can make tea and popcorn and read.

When she arrives at work she is right on time, but Sara Page stops her in the hall, her face smiling but faintly disapproving. "Janine," she said, and she is shaking her head in what certainly she means to be a kindly way. "Janine, we had coffee again this morning, did you forget?" The wide, powdered face is swaying, clucking over her, Janine has "forgotten" Monday morning coffee with the other secretaries yet again and Janine thinks fast. "I had a doctor's appointment, Sara," and this seems to satisfy, there is that faint look of concern and Sara backs off. "We'll see you next week, then," and Janine smiles absently but she is thinking of all the caked lipstick and coffee, the clouds of smoke in the little conference room where they gather and she knows she won't go next week or the next. They will talk of boyfriends and husbands and children. Even if she prepared they wouldn't care about what she knows now, the information on bears or the facts she can recite on botany, on Berlin. She would have nothing to say.

Home. She is home again, and she takes off her shoes, pulls off her skirt and the white blouse with the little flapped tie. She puts on Holst's "Planets," and naked, she dances around the ring that is made by her dining room, living room, kitchen. She is thinking of the fairies, the princesses, and in the music, the pounding of Mars, warlike Mars, she is part of the dream.

She is working her way through the Cs now, through cactus and Calcutta, while outside the season is changing, she can see it through the bus window, summer leavening into fall.

But this morning she awakens early, her stomach grinding with pain. She has the flu, the aching muscles and the inability to keep down toast or even lukewarm tea. When she calls in to work, her voice is so fluid with nausea that Sara Page is sympathetic, even warm over the phone. And so Janine stays home not one day but two. It is a treat, a luxury once the nausea has passed and she has only weakness to contend with. She cannot read the first day, she is too tired, but on the second morning she opens her encyclopedia where the flower bookmark is, and the entry is CANCER.

When Janine returns to work there is a surprising flurry of concern from Sara Page and the other girls. Perhaps it is not concern, only curiosity, since she has never in five years called in sick, never. But Janine still feels a subtle thrill and perhaps it is this that makes her pull Sara aside and lie to her. "I had another doctor's appointment, Sara. They are doing some tests."

And now Janine has something to talk about, because each day when she comes in Sara or one of the other girls is pulling close. "Janine how are you, have you heard anything?" It is in this way that Janine begins to come early on Mondays. She sits with the other women, eating the greasy doughnuts from a pasteboard box, and she is a celebrity of sorts because she has something to say. It is not until mid-October that the lie expands.

She has gone to the library, done to her research—she knows the symptoms, the pain. She has been reading about the disease but also her fairy tales and she believes that fairies are helping her when she comes in for doughnuts, her face pale and hectic, and announces, "I have cancer. I have cancer."

Sara and the women, not more than girls most of them, cluster and chatter. "Janine, no! It can't be. Get another opinion." And Janine is the center of it, exultant eye in a hurricane of tight skirts and smoky breath. She is not sure the concern is sincere but it doesn't matter. She is thinking, *I am I am I am.*

Janine stops eating the doughnuts. No more popcorn at night, either, she has to lose weight—it is part of the dream. She no longer wears make-up. Her bare face looks older but it is worth it the way the women cluck over the circles under her eyes. And sometimes when she gets home at night there is a message on the machine from one of the girls at the office. And when she comes in to work one morning there is a card on her desk from Sara's small daughter: a crayoned sun and the words GET WELL scrawled in blue.

By December Janine has lost fifteen pounds and Sara stops her in the hallway. "Janine, there is a cancer support group you may want to call," and Janine does. And her voice is hesitant, halting on the phone, but it is only because of her extreme good fortune—she is edgy with it—the woman on the phone is so kind, urging her to join them. *I am*, Janine is thinking as she hangs up the phone, *I am armed with fairies—this circle of friends will be ready-made.*

Responding Personally

1. With another student, talk about your thoughts and feelings as you were reading this story.
2. Write a paragraph, giving reasons why you think a person might pretend to be ill.

Responding Critically

3. What is the motivation for the lie? Explain in a paragraph response.
4. For small group discussion: Recalling details from the story, what impression do you have of the main character? Is she ignorant? Dangerous? Mentally unstable?
5. What kind of reaction does Janine get from the other women at work when she pretends to be ill? Is their response realistic? What makes it possible for her to deceive them? Explain your ideas.
6. In a sense, the cancer is more symbolic than imaginary. Explain how the symbol relates to the theme.

Responding Creatively

7. Compose a "spam" e-mail message for Janine's online friends, updating them about her latest condition.
8. Assume that it is now six months later. Write a sequel to the story in which Janine is no longer showing any signs of

cancer. As a dialogue, write the comments her fellow workers make to her. How does she respond to them? Share the dialogue with those classmates have written. How are the dialogues similar and different?

Problem-Solving/Decision-Making

9. In your opinion, what help does Janine need in order to make her happier? As her psychologist, write a prescription for the ingredients she needs to make her feel better.

As I drove I could see my father's face in the windshield caught there by some trick of light and dark.

Robert Hilles
Aero Bars

I visit my father in the hospital while he is getting chemotherapy, and I bring him three Aero bars. I am reminded of the time when I was burnt in the fire and he would visit me every night bringing an Aero bar, placing it on the table for me and I would always wait until he said good bye and was gone down the corridor before I would open it and take a bite. He would never prod me to eat it while he was there, understanding in some unexplainable way. Today, as I sat in the hospital looking out over the green park across the street, the IV dripped into my father, and I could see him when I was a boy, the sun shining on a Saturday morning, him standing with one foot on the fender of his 51 Ford half ton, the sunlight bringing his face fully alive. He didn't say much, just smiled and chuckled to himself and then would get in the truck and drive away. He laughed today as I told him a joke. The teenager in the next bed had his appendix out and the phone kept ringing for him, never a call for my father, just for that young man. My father sat so patiently in the hospital, letting the IV pour into him, believing with all his life that this, if nothing else, could save him. My mother and I took the elevator back down the street and we embraced, neither shedding tears, as we supported one another. Knees trembling a little as the elevator touched ground. We didn't say much as we crossed the parking lot and I tried to find his window again to wave up but the declining sunlight filled each one and I could see nothing but an uncomfortable glare dancing off those shimmering pieces of glass and my mother and I bumped against each other as we walked towards the car. It waited there like a dead thing, doors creaking open as we each selected our appropriate side, one slamming the door after the other and I backed the car away from its parking spot as if I could leave certain portions of my life behind and cut away from it and head somewhere else. As I drove I could see my father's face in the windshield caught there by some trick of light and dark. I could trace his every feature, watch his eyes as they took in the horizon, not filled by it alone for each thing has an appropriate place in his life as he lays patiently on the bed, hardly making a sound. Most of what he has done has been accomplished in silence, his eyes, seeking me, sometimes fixing on me in a way that could make me uncomfortable or happy, depending on how I looked away. As we were driving on the highway a few days earlier, I was rubbing my father's back and I was reminded of when I was a teenager and we'd sit, I in his arms watching TV and I realized that I'd forgotten the tenderness we shared all those years, instead, I built up an amazing fabric of lies. He fooled me too. I was afraid even as I grew older. I see his eyes are tired as he laughs at my silly jokes, and tries hard to show me that he loved me and it was me that backed away all those years, it was me who took away the things he wanted and discarded and left behind everything else, it was me that didn't say I love you. As I stood beside my father, laughing on the Cancer Ward, I was taken in by those blue eyes and I wanted to touch each one to find with my fingers a slight hint of what they saw, instead, I lifted a hand to his cheek and stroked it. He smiled a little, his gaze drawn away from the IV drip for a little while. He looked almost happy, except what drained into him was now a complete mystery, his life being filled with things he wasn't really expecting and I turned away once more, backing out to the door embracing only for a moment then backing downstairs.

Later I stood at the mirror, balancing my hat awkwardly on my head. I moved it first to my left side and then to my right side, just as I saw my father doing a few hours earlier when I had offered him one of my hats and as I watched something in me was set free. At the mirror I saw that I was trying so hard to be my father, to be the things not that he had taught me but things I have noticed as he passed me in the house, the things I'd seen those few days when I was alone in the hospital and he would come with the Aero bar and it's not because I praise it that I want to be that, but because in all of that, in all of the learning, the studying, the unraveling of his life into my life, and my life into my children's and their lives into other lives, in all that massive unraveling, something got put back into place, something we didn't even notice until turning back we could see it there, glistening, just as it ought to be in full view, showing us the way we'd come.

Responding Personally

1. Write about how you feel or think you would feel when visiting someone in the hospital.
2. If you have read "Cancer," (page 205) explain how this story's treatment of the cancer topic is different from the previous one.

Responding Critically

3. List the story's events in chronological order.
4. For paragraph response: Why do you think the son brings an Aero bar to his father? What does the Aero bar symbolize to them? Why?
5. As the story progresses, what insights does the son gain into his relationship with his father? In the last paragraph, decide what it is that the son realizes. Share your understandings with those of another classmate.
6. For discussion: Should the author have used a more conventional style of paragraphing in this story? Why do you think he made the paragraphing choice that he did?

Responding Creatively

7. In pairs, role-play the last visit of the son to the father in the hospital.
8. Prepare a live reading of this story with appropriate taped background music. Present your version to the class.

Problem-Solving/Decision-Making

9. For written personal response: Describe a relationship in your life that changed over a period of time and the decisions that you made to keep the relationship vital and lasting.

"Have you no shame? How can you go exhibit yourself like that? It's not decent," she repeated.

Marta Jara
The Dress

Translated by Martha J. Manier

"It's them." She knew immediately. She raised her head over the full-grown plants and watched. "It's them!" The peddler and his wife. At that very moment they were heading over to sit on a rock shaded by a myrtle tree. "Yes it is ..." she repeated, looking at them through the dark green tide of the potato patch.

She was crouched down, hilling up the potatoes and weeding along the rows on a low and not-too-distant rise.

She saw the man—he was not very tall—set his bag by the tree. He was wiping his face with a white rag. Perhaps a handkerchief. "He's wiping off sweat," she guessed. "It must be hot to walk the roads with such a heavy load."

His wife had just sat down in the myrtle's shade.

"They'll probably rest and then go down by the stream," she guessed. "If I take the road to the gate, I'll see them when they come by."

She knew she was deceiving herself. "That's not it. It's not just to see them." Turning her head, she cast a glance over her shoulder. Down below in the middle of the apple orchard the house seemed deserted except for the geese standing guard and solemnly walking in a row along the edge of the irrigation ditch. "Where can she be? She's probably inside. That's it. And she won't want ... she's never wanted ..." she grumbled as she bent down, her face tense and sad. Her lips trembled. "She'll die some day, but not soon enough for me to toast the occasion. I, too, will feel old—left with no company but the dog, the cat, the birds and the constant planting and hilling of potatoes. For what? For whom?" Suddenly she understood. "She's had everything she's denying me."

Before thinking it, almost as if anticipating it, she dropped her hilling tool and began to run through the potato patch, down the rise, and toward the house.

When she sped by, the startled geese cackled. She didn't stop but kept on running until she reached the barred gate. She straightened her dress and stepped into the ditch to wash off her feet. "They still haven't arrived. I have time to wash my face," she calculated. She smoothed back her hair. She wore it in a single braid that weighed against her back. She was a mature woman, strong, and robust like a man, with white skin and a sour, nervous face. She was barefoot. In the islands, the milky whiteness of her skin was rare.

"They have to come this way," she comforted herself. "There's no other road." She leaned against the fence post. A pleasant breeze blew and refreshed her hard, muscular legs, which were furrowed by swollen, blue veins.

"They have to come this way," she repeated, "and this time I will indeed buy a dress. Although she'll be opposed to the idea, I will buy it, to go to Chonchi to church on Sundays. I'll go after a good bath, with my hair combed and with my dress. They'll notice me. Somebody, somebody has to notice. I don't care if he is from Chiloe ... He'll be a man ... And although she'll be opposed ..."

They were coming. She could hear their steps, their stumbling on the stones, the woman's chatter. She unconsciously smoothed her hair again. Her greeting surprised them. They approached. The man leaned his bag against the fence post before answering.

"Yes, yes. Good clothes. Would you like to look?" he offered. Then he looked at the woman accompanying him, seeming to indicate "You deal with this one."

"Where shall I show you the clothes?" It was the woman who spoke. "Surely you'll want to try something on. Isn't that right?"

"No, I won't. She probably won't let me buy anything." She threw an apprehensive glance over her shoulder and behind her in the doorway her mother was waiting. "I knew it," she said to herself. And making up her mind she suddenly lifted the bars to the gate.

"Come in."

She heard the man say to the woman, "You go. I'll wait down the road a little."

"What are you selling?" the cold, dry question stopped them at the door. She held her arms crossed over her chest, and like her voice her eyes glimmered with a slight irony.

"A little bit of everything. Used clothing, needles, thread, buttons, combs, soap, mirrors ..." the itinerant trader recited her wares in a monotonous tone.

"We don't need anything," she interrupted. Without moving, she blocked any access to the house, her despotic tone of voice containing a quality stronger than her very presence there before the closed door. Her look was mocking.

"Ah. Excuse me ... I thought your daughter said...." she stammered, nodding toward her daughter.

"I knew it. I didn't need to hear her say it. She won't let me. She's always, her entire life, been this way: selfish."

The old woman smiled disdainfully. The result was a tension-filled silence.

"They hate each other," the peddler's wife guessed. She shrugged her shoulders. Ready to wait, she rested her bag on the ground.

"Mother, I wanted ... They have dresses. I need one. I have the money. It's mine. I've earned it working. You know one never has a chance...."

She didn't finish the sentence and stared at the old woman, who understood her look: "You've been silent for so many years," it said, "and now finally you are letting go."

She confronted her. "It's an opportunity," she said. "You know full well that in town there are no ..."

"Opportunity!" the old woman laughed and scathingly added, "Is that what you think?" But she moved away from the door, yielding but not backing down, as if to say, "Okay, see for yourself. Try it."

They entered the house. They walked along a dark hall, a closed door on each side, and there, beyond, at the end, a room equally dark but cool and spacious. On the wooden walls hanging from thick rusted nails were diverse farm implements. From the beams drooped nets and fishing gear, strings of mussels and dried, smoked meats. The woman examined it all with curiosity while feigning disinterest.

"You can put your things here," the old lady grunted, pointing to a round table with no cloth but dappled by the light filtering in the window. Through the foliage of an apple tree that nearly deprived the room of all light, you could see the garden.

She began to unpack her wares and scatter them haphazardly on top of the table. "What do these two women do here before the stove in winter, always face-to-face and dragging out their hatred?" she thought. "Just as there's a God in heaven, they probably fight the whole live-long day."

The spinster approached. She felt, although without seeing it, her mother's sardonic grimace. Not even the darkest shadows could hide it. "It doesn't matter. This time she won't be able to stop me. I'll wash real good and do my hair, and when I go to church, I'll put on my new dress. Somebody, yes, somebody, will have to notice me, if only because of the dress. 'Look!' they'll say, 'Isn't that Eloisa? She must have money!' I don't care what they say. I'm forty-six years old and have some good land, a house, a boat, animals. My mother is old … it'll be enough for them to see me and they'll think … it doesn't matter to me you're here laughing. I have the right to have a man … just like you did. Be that as it may …" She picked out the dresses. Rather she rummaged through them haphazardly, almost without knowing what she was doing, confused by her own thoughts and her mother's inimical presence.

"The old woman's making her confused," the peddler thought, and she came to Eloisa's aid. "Let's see. This one should fit you just fine."

She held the dress up to Eloisa. She was amazed, for she herself was small and slight. "What a big woman! How can she be so big? If she tries them on, she's surely going to split the seams." With the patience necessary to her trade, she began to look for the ones she thought were of an adequate size.

"They aren't decent," the dry, clipped voice of the old woman lashed out systematically. "They aren't suitable," she smiled, savoring her triumph. "Have you no shame? How can you go exhibit yourself like that? It's not decent," she repeated.

They found one. Not very pretty, a solid color, pale green, faded from wear. She grew quiet. She couldn't say it was indecent. It was closed up to the neck, and its long, puckered sleeves hung down awkwardly. Leaving her corner, she came up to touch it and find fault. It would be too tight for her and the material, now worn thin, couldn't withstand the stress.

"It won't last you one wearing. You'll come back from Chonchi in tatters," she predicted.

Nevertheless, it was she who found the solution. Unintentionally, and unconsciously, her femininity, who knows for how long suppressed and forgotten, surged: a blue cloth attracted her, the thick-linen of a skirt. She couldn't help but touch it.

"Ah!" the seller exclaimed. "How stupid of me not to have remembered! This will fit you just fine. Try it on. The material is of a high quality."

She was indecisive. She wanted a dress not a skirt.

"Try it on!" her mother ordered. Her little eyes laughed sarcastically. "You don't like it, do you? It doesn't matter. It won't do for what you want it for, but it will be just fine for work." And directing herself to the other woman, she asked, "How much is it?"

"One thousand. One thousand pesos," she stated explicitly.

"Oh, no! That's high!" She didn't say anymore, but that was enough to let them know she wouldn't give in.

"That's what it's worth," the woman responded without praising her merchandise. She presumed the sale would develop like a long, difficult sparring match.

"We can't pay that much. 500. Not a peso more."

"The old lady is stubborn, but she's not going to get the better of me. If I tell her 800, I'm lost. I will have to let her raise her offer." And to reinforce her position, she said, "No. One thousand. I asked a fair price. I can't sell it for less."

They contemplated each other: two cocks, ready for the fight, facing off, looking for trouble. The daughter entered. The mother made her turn around and again examined the cloth, touching it. Unexpectedly she offered, "Perhaps you would like a cup of tea?"

She caught the seller, and even her daughter, off guard.

"Yes, thank you. Why not." Her empty stomach was what ventured an answer. She hadn't had lunch, the morning was drawing on, and her man would probably be making a fire somewhere around there.

"She doesn't want ... she won't let me pay so much. I know her ..." the spinster informed her with a bitter expression, after her mother was gone. She touched the skirt as if caressing an already dissipated dream.

"I can let you have it for 800," she conceded. "Not a peso less. If you can't pay it, you'd take it off."

"She won't want to. I know her," she said disheartened and added to herself, "She's as stubborn as a mule." Suddenly her face lit up. She spoke quickly and softly, whispering. "In front of her, let me have it for 500; later, outside on the road, I'll give you the difference." She didn't manage to explain any more; she barely had time to shut her mouth. Her mother entered bringing a steaming cup and in her eyes an inquisitive and malicious expression. She deposited the tea on the table.

"Sit down," she invited. "Help yourself." She put the sugar within reach and remained standing, observing them. She smelled something gone on, but wily as a fox, she asked no questions.

The other woman began to sip her tea slowly. She praised it, wanting to flatter. After a while, as if the cup of tea had softened her, the tradeswoman pointed to the daughter. "I'll let you have it for 800."

Unflappable, the old woman replied, "No. 500."

She kept drinking the tea slowly. Why hurry? She had her technique and now she would let the old lady witness it.

Unable to contain herself the spinster approached the table, still wearing the skirt. Mute and looking annoyed, she began to rifle through the dresses.

"It just may be that this fool will ruin everything." She hurried and drank the rest of the tea in a single gulp and stood up. The old woman was looking at her out of the corner of her eye when the peddler surprised her by saying, "Well, what do you think is a fair price?" As she asked her question, she proceeded to pack.

"500. Not a peso more."

"But mother! I ..."

"Take it off!" she demanded, energetically interrupting.

"All right, I'll let you have it for 500," the woman acceded, "to repay your kindness. For no other reason."

"Go, bring the money!" she ordered, spitting out the words with a disdainful bitterness that seemed to imply, "This is what you get, and it's not the dress." She again sat down in her chair in the corner, from where she oversaw the payment. She smelled the trap but couldn't detect it. They said their good-byes. The seller gathered up her things and, unaccompanied, she headed toward the hall.

"I'll wait for her outside on the road. This one won't trick me. She's not capable," she deduced. She left. When she closed the door, she could hear the old woman say, "Go with her down to the road."

They walked together following the path alongside the irrigation ditches.

"There below, where she won't be able to see us, I'll give you what I owe you," the spinster whispered. "She must still be watching us." Then she surprised the woman by saying, "I've been thinking about you for days. I saw you in Chonchi. And from that day on I've been telling myself, 'This is my chance.' If I have a new dress, it's possible someone will notice me. Even though he's from Chiloe. We—and my mother notes the difference—are descended from Spaniards. Once I had a suitor. My mother was opposed: 'A Chilote,' she said. 'Never. I would rather see you dead!' That was many years ago. I never had another chance." She talked without stopping, telling all the essentials, exposing her life in short sentences. "I'm forty-six years old. I'm getting old. It has to be now. Although he may be from Chiloe, he's still a man. A man is a man, and my mother is now old. My father died, and one day I will inherit all this." She gestured, attempting to show the property with a sweep of her arm. "Anyone can understand that I will inherit all this. I just need someone to notice me, that's all. That's why I wanted the dress. To go to Chonchi."

The peddler, worn out by the weight of her bag, listened without looking at the speaker's face. Astounded, she heard her out. She saw only the bare feet, leaving in the dust wide footprints, the firm mannish step.

"That's why I wanted a dress. It's more noticeable than a skirt," she pointed out regretfully.

They arrived at the gate.

"Come on. Come with me a bit more," the peddler's wife insisted, pointing to a nearby spot. Surely around the bend her man would be waiting for her. She stopped. "He doesn't have to know," she told herself, taking the money for the skirt and keeping it. "He'll never notice." Then she opened her bag and began to take out clothes. She found it almost at once. She unfolded a red blouse and put it in the spinster's hands.

"Here, this will fit you nicely and it looks good with the skirt. It will draw attention but it's decent," she said, employing for the first time the Chiloean expression. "Put it on when you go to Chonchi. It's a present." She warned her: "Don't show it to your mother, don't tell her a thing. She's capable of ripping it up. And when you find what you're looking for, whoever he may be, do what you have to do and don't be scared. You're too old to be afraid of your mother."

She didn't wait to be thanked. She left the spinster, stunned, in the middle of the road. She walked off. Beyond, on the side toward the beach, was a column of smoke waiting for her like a signal. "There's my husband," she told herself. Before rounding the bend, she looked back. The woman was still standing there, embracing the blouse as if it were a man.

Responding Personally

1. How do you feel about the daughter at the end of the story? Will her life change for the better? Why or why not? Compare your responses with those of a classmate.
2. Write a paragraph about an object or possession which you once really desired. Why was it important to you?

Responding Critically

3. For discussion: Describe the conflicts in this story. Are they ultimately resolved? Why does the woman embrace the dress at the conclusion of the story? Will she fulfil her dream?
4. Explain the relationship between the mother and daughter. How do you think it got that way? Will it change after the peddler's visit?
5. With a partner, consider the motivation of the peddler's wife. Why does she do what she does at the end of the story? What do we learn of her character from this action?
6. Write a character sketch of either the mother or her daughter.

Responding Creatively

7. Write a sequel to the story in which the daughter goes to church in her new outfit. Compare your sequel with ones other students have written. What different predictions have been made in your sequels?
8. As the daughter, write a thank-you letter a month later to the peddler's wife.

Problem-Solving/Decision-Making

9. Assume the daughter goes to see a family psychologist about her problems with her mother. Write the advice that the psychologist might offer to help her cope better with her mother.

I wanted to know if he was smiling, but I'll never know.

Lesley Choyce

The Third or Fourth Happiest Man in Nova Scotia

The first time I saw Ray Doucette he was climbing up a thirty-foot spruce tree out by the mouth of the inlet. The top of the tree had been sheared right off by the lightning, and just below the damage was a giant nest. Ray was climbing up to that nest, his boots slipping on the wet branches and his hands clutching each new hold like vice-grips. He was carrying something in a red handkerchief pouch that dangled from his mouth. Inside the pouch was some frightened creature that was screeching like a banshee.

I was afraid to say a word. Finally, Ray looped one arm over a lightning-splintered branch and lowered his head until his package sat snugly back in the nest. Then, just as the screeching subsided from one source, it rose again tenfold from out of the sky. Ray lost his footing and hung by one armpit as his feet kicked the empty air.

The mother eagle made a lunge for Ray and knocked his hat off. Then it flew upward, hovered, tucked its wings, and dove straight for Ray's face. Ray didn't flinch. I just closed my eyes and heard one god-awful shriek. Then nothing.

When I looked up, the mother eagle was sitting perfectly still on her young one returned to the nest. Ray was smiling eyeball to eyeball with the giant bird, and his one free hand was petting it on the neck. I could just barely make out that he was singing something. "Rock-a-bye baby."

Ray Doucette lived with his wife, Adele, in an old crooked house near the head of Tom Lurcher Inlet. He had a tumble-down wharf, and every day of the year when the seas allowed, he went out fishing in his boat.

It was such a deceptive little inlet, with jutting rocks and an incorrigible channel, that more respectable fishermen had given up on the place long ago. I once asked Ray about the problems with negotiating the inlet. He said, "Well, the channel's just like a snake that's got its back broke in maybe twenty-five places. And, when you get to the mouth, if you don't plant the boat dead between the gull rock and the Cannonballs, you'll run aground." The Cannonballs, he explained, was a hidden shoal of perfectly round rocks that shifted around with the storms and the seasons.

"Did you ever think of moving to another inlet?" I asked.

He looked at me like I just told him that he should try eating arsenic for breakfast. "This is one of the deepest, cleanest, most interesting channels on the Eastern Shore," he told me.

Altogether, twelve families had lived in the ramshackle houses on either side of Ray in years past. But the families were all gone. The men had taken city jobs or moved off to fish inlets less interesting than Tom Lurcher.

It was around the time of the exodus that Ray had married Adele. She had grown up in the house next door. Adele, so the story goes, just moved in with Ray when everyone else moved away. Ray said that it was Adele who had made him the third or fourth happiest man in Nova Scotia. All you had to do was look into her blue, summer-sea eyes and feel better about living. Adele entered Ray's life with a rooster and a hen.

Aside from Adele moving in with him, I don't think Ray paid much attention to all the other families moving out. He always paid more heed to wind direction than neighbours, anyway. He hauled in his fish, checked the oil in his engine and went about his life as usual.

Then the rooster got sick. "I hadn't thought that much above living things up till that. I guess he was mean the way roosters are, and he was always underfoot. But I couldn't stand to see him die." So Ray nursed the rooster back to health by feeding him fish oil and corn flour. After the rooster recovered, Ray sometimes took the bird out to sea with him on calm days. The rooster recovered so well that Ray had thirty other chickens by the end of that first year. They gave the chickens the Slaunwhite house to live in and the chickens seemed to like it fine.

By the time I met Ray, the rooster was gone, dead, but his descendants roamed freely up and down Tom Lurcher Inlet. It was impossible to walk across Ray's yard without stepping on eggs. Adele could never keep up with which ones were fresh and which ones were old, so most of the eggs got fed to the gulls.

The first sea gull came into Ray's life when a hunter arrived at the inlet from the city. The hunter couldn't see any ducks, so he started shooting at a couple of Ray's chickens. The chickens were too quick for the hunter and took cover in the mossy rocks. But the gulls weren't as wily. Pretty soon the hunter had shot the wing off one herring gull. Ray was just snaking his boat back in from the sea when he saw it fall out of the sky. He steered toward the wounded gull, knowing full well he might tear the bottom out of his boat.

Sure enough, Ray's boat plowed into something and she started to leak. But he fished the gull out of the sea and got his boat back to his wharf before it sank and settled on the bottom. The gull, of course, was big and mean as only three-year-old herring gulls can be, and it tore into Ray's wrist like a chainsaw into softwood.

The hunter saw Ray at his wharf in the sinking boat and came over to see what was going on. There was Ray dripping blood from the wrist, standing waist-deep in the cold water that had sucked up the deck of his boat. The hunter asked Ray what happened. When Ray explained that he had saved the seagull, the hunter just laughed, called him a fool and then drove off.

Adele had to stitch up Ray's wrist with twenty-pound test fishing line, and Ray had never been prouder of his wife. The one-winged gull lived, and, once Ray got his boat seaworthy again, it fed happily every day on cod heads and mackerel guts.

News seemed to have leaked out to the gull community up and down the shore because injured birds kept turning up. One gull had swallowed a fishing hook, another had lost a leg. Some had broken wings that could be set with splints and tape. Others arrived with no outward signs of injury but stayed on nonetheless. Many of the creatures that arrived could live outside, but some seemed to want housing, so the empty village was turned into a rest home for injured animals.

By the time I met Ray, he had maybe twenty-five birds. His arrival home from sea each day was heralded with raucous, enthusiastic approval. Ray loved it. He had also taken to hiking the shoreline with Adele looking for creatures that needed help. Together they adopted a porcupine without teeth, an anorexic heron, a blind otter, wild rabbits that were missing body parts from snares, and an assortment of small birds crippled in various ways by the cruelty of men and nature.

When Adele died, the doctor told Ray, "It was something she was born with. There was nothing you or I could have done about it."

Ray said, "But that's not right."

The doctor just shook his head. "Sometimes it happens that way."

Ray told me that he just sat at the kitchen table with a cold cup of tea in his hand and didn't move for four days. "I'd of sat there like that, too," he said, "except that the gulls began to swarm all over the roof. And the heron kept staring at me through the window. And when I opened the door, the yard was a sea of hungry chickens."

Then, one day, a planner from the government drove the rutted lane down to Ray's house. He'd never seen so many one-winged gulls and maimed creatures in his life. When Ray walked over, the planner rolled down his window and tried to explain something. But the words just went in one ear and out the other. Whatever it was the man was talking about, Ray decided to pay no attention.

When I read about the harbour development program in the paper, I knew Ray was in for big trouble. Somebody had determined that Tom Lurcher Inlet had one of the deepest, cleanest, most interesting channels on the whole shore. The channel would just have to be dredged and straightened, the article said, and they'd blast the Cannonball Shoal to smithereens if they had to.

Ray was heaving fish heads to his gulls on the morning I told him the news. He didn't believe me. "What do they want this place for?"

"They want to put in a new wharf and bring more boats back."

"But nobody lives here."

"They will," I explained.

Ray received notices in the mail, but he refused to read them. Then the planner drove up again, this time with a Mountie.

The man pointed to Ray's house. "We're willing to make an offer ..." But Ray didn't listen to the rest.

He got in his boat and headed to sea. The tide was wrong and he barely squeaked past the Cannonballs without ripping the engine out of her. I hired Bill Mannette to take me to sea to look for Ray. We saw Ray's boat beached at Riley's Island. When we came in close, I jumped out and ran up and down the beach, finally finding Ray sitting alone on a drift log.

"This one's not right, either," Ray said. "But I'll keep looking." Ray pulled a wad of two-dollar bills out of his pants and shoved it into my hand. "Feed my creatures. I'll be back in a while." I tried to talk him into coming back now, but he'd have none of it.

I kept an eye on Ray's creatures, but I couldn't get any of them to eat. I was sitting on Ray's back step looking to sea when his boat appeared. The chickens and gulls exploded into life. I held my ears and covered my head. The gulls that could fly made a beeline toward the boat. Ray pulled up tight to the dock, cut the motor.

"I found it," he said.

He'd say nothing more. He fed his creatures from a boatload of fresh cod and over the next week built a barge out of wood from Adele's first house. I offered to help, but he wouldn't let me lift a finger.

Ray took his time about what he was doing. I checked in every day, but he had little to say to me. It was about a week later that I heard the bulldozer thundering down the lane to Tom Lurcher Inlet. I ran down the path to Ray's wharf, but I was too late.

Ray's boat, towing his barge full of animals, was on a slow, zigzag path to sea. A whirlpool of sea gulls swirled above the boat in the bright blue sky. I waved, but I don't think he noticed me. I wanted to see his face, but he was too far away. I wanted to know if he was smiling, but I'll never know. The boat and the barge passed by the Cannonballs and on beyond the lightning-splintered tree at the mouth of the inlet. Ray turned neither east nor west but went straight south until he was lost in the squint of the sun and the swell of the sea.

Responding Personally

1. Describe a time when you or someone you know looked after an injured bird or other wildlife.
2. Who are some famous people who have devoted their lives to working with, studying, and preserving wildlife?

Responding Critically

3. With another student, discuss what happens to Ray at the end of the story. Is this indeterminate ending appropriate for this story and character? Explain.
4. For discussion: What does the story reveal about Ray's character? Is he a good man or just confused? Is he caring and genuine, or simply obsessed? In a paragraph, offer your analysis of the protagonist's character.
5. What is your opinion of the narrator? What is his function in the story? How does he contrast to Ray?

6. Explain what Ray means when he says that he is the third or fourth happiest man in Nova Scotia? Is there any other sense in which that is true? Compare your explanation with those of classmates.

Responding Creatively

7. Compose a ballad about Ray, the doctor for injured sea birds.
8. Write a letter nominating Ray for an animal activist award. Give reasons for his nomination and examples of his work.

Problem-Solving/Decision-Making

9. Prepare a first draft of a speech intended for a group of kindergarten students, describing strategies for being kinder to animals.

They said that I kept the baby for four hours that morning.

Luci Tapahonso
All the Colors of Sunset

Even after all this time, when I look back at all that happened, I don't know if I would do anything differently. That summer morning seemed like any other. The sun came up over the mountain around seven or so, and when I went to throw the coffee grounds out, I put the pouch of corn pollen in my apron pocket so that I could pray before I came inside.

During the summers, we sleep most nights in the *chaha'oh,* the shadehouse, unless it rains. I remembered early that morning I had heard loud voices yelling and they seemed to come from the north. Whoever it was quieted quickly, and I fell asleep. Right outside the *chaha'oh,* I knew the dogs were alert—their ears erect and eyes glistening. Out here near Rockpoint, where we live, it's so quiet and isolated that we can hear things from a far distance. It's mostly desert and the huge rocks nearby, *tsé ahil ah neeé,* whale rock and the other rocks, seem to bounce noises into the valley. People live far apart and there are no streetlights nearby. The nights are quiet, except for animal and bird noises, and the sky is always so black. In the Navajo way, they say the night sky is made of black jet, and that the folding darkness comes from the north. Sometimes in the evenings, I think of this when the sun is setting, and all the bright colors fall somewhere into the west. Then I let the beauty of the sunset go, and my sadness along with it.

That morning I fixed a second pot of coffee, and peeled potatoes to fry. Just as I finished slicing the potatoes, I thought I heard my grandbaby cry. I went out and looked out toward my daughter's home. She lives across the arroyo a little over a mile away. I shaded my eyes and squinted—the sun was in her direction. Finally, I went inside and finished fixing breakfast. We were going to go into Chinle that afternoon, so I didn't go over to their house.

Later that morning, I was polishing some pieces of jewelry when I heard my daughter crying outside. My heart quickened. I rushed to the door and she practically fell inside the house. She was carrying the baby in her cradleboard and could hardly talk—she was sobbing and screaming so. I grabbed the baby, knowing she was hurt. When I looked at my granddaughter, I knew the terrible thing that had happened. Her little face was so pale and wet from crying. I could not think or speak—somehow I found my way to the south wall of the hooghan and sat down, still holding my sweet baby. My first and only grandchild was gone.

I held her close and nuzzled her soft neck. I sang over and over the little songs that I always sang to her. I unwrapped her and touched slowly, slowly every part of her little smooth body. I wanted to remember every sweet detail and said aloud each name like I had always done, "*Díí nijáád wolyé, sho'wéé.*" This is called your leg, my baby. I asked her, "*Nits'iiyah sha'*?" and nuzzled the back of her neck like before. "*Jo ka i.*" This time she did not giggle and laugh. I held her and rocked, and sang, and talked to her.

The pollen pouch was still in my pocket, and I put a bit into her mouth as I would have done when her first tooth came in. I put a pinch of pollen on her head as I would have done when she first left for kindergarten. I put a pinch of pollen in her little hands as I would have done when she was given her first lamb, as I would have done when she was given her own colt. This way she would have been gentle and firm with her pets. I brushed her with an eagle feather as I would have done when she graduated from junior high. All this and so much more that could have been swept over me as I sat there leaning over my little grandbaby.

She was almost five months old, and had just started to recognize me. She cried for me to hold her and I tried to keep her with me as much as I could. Sometimes I took her for long walks and showed her everything, and told her little stories about the birds and animals we saw. She would fall asleep on our way home, and still I hummed and sang softly. I couldn't stop singing. For some reason, when she was born, I was given so much time for her. I guess that's how it is with grandparents. I wasn't ever too busy to care for her. When my daughter took her home, my house seemed so empty and quiet.

They said that I kept the baby for four hours that morning. My daughter left and then returned with her husband. They were afraid to bother me in my grief. I don't remember much of it. I didn't know how I acted, or maybe that was the least of what I was conscious of. My daughter said later that I didn't say one word to her. I don't remember.

Finally, I got up and gave the baby to them so they could go to the hospital at Chinle. I followed in my own truck, and there the doctor confirmed her death, and we began talking about what we had to do next. Word spread quickly. When I went to buy some food at Basha's, several people comforted me and helped me with the shopping. My sisters and two aunts were at my home when I returned. They had straightened up the house, and were cooking already. Some of my daughters-in-law were cooking and getting things ready in the *chaha'oh* outside. By that evening, the house and the *chaha'oh* were filled with people—our own relatives, clan relatives, friends from school, church, and the baby's father's kin. People came and held me, comforting me and murmuring their sympathies. They cried with me, and brought me plates of food. I felt like I was in a daze—I hardly spoke. I tried to help cook and serve, but was gently guided back to the armchair that had somehow become "my chair" since that morning.

There were meetings each day, and various people stood up to counsel and advise everyone who was there, including my daughter and her husband. When everything was done, and we had washed our faces and started over again, I couldn't seem to focus on things. Before all this happened, I was very busy each day—cooking, sewing, taking out the horses sometimes, feeding the animals, and often just visiting with people. One of my children or my sisters always came by and we would talk and laugh while I continued my tasks. Last winter was a good year for piñons so I was still cleaning and roasting the many flour sackfuls we had picked. At Many Farms junction, some people from Shiprock had a truckload of the sweetest corn I had ever tasted, so I bought plenty and planned to make *ntsidigodí* and other kinds of cornbread. We would have these tasty delicacies to eat in the winter. We liked to remember summer by the food we had stored and preserved.

When we were little, my mother taught all of us girls to weave, but I hadn't touched a loom in years. When I became a grandmother, I began to think of teaching some of the old things to my baby. Maybe it was my age, but I remembered a lot of the things we were told. Maybe it was that I was alone more than I had ever been—my children were grown. My husband passed on five years ago, and since I was by myself and I had enough on which to live, I stopped working at a paying job.

After all this happened, I resumed my usual tasks and tried to stay busy so that my grandbaby's death wouldn't overwhelm me. I didn't cry or grieve out loud because they say that one can call the dead back by doing that. Yet so much had changed, and it was as if I was far away from everything. Some days I fixed a lunch and took the sheep out for the day and returned as the sun was going down. And when I came back inside, I realized that I hadn't spoken to the animals all day. It seemed strange, and yet I just didn't feel like talking. The dogs would follow me around, wanting attention—for me to throw a stick for them, or talk to them—then after a while they would just lie down and watch me. Once I cleaned and roasted a pan of piñons perfectly without thinking about it. It's a wonder that I didn't burn myself. A few weeks later, we had to brand some colts, and give the horses shots, so everyone got together and we spent the day at the corral in the dust and heat. Usually it was a happy and noisy time, but that day was quieter than usual. At least we had taken care of everything.

Sometimes I dreamt of my grandbaby, and it was as if nothing had happened. In my dreams, I carried her around, singing and talking to her. She smiled and giggled at me. When I awoke, it was as if she had been lying beside me, kicking and reaching around. A small space beside me would be warm, and her scent faint. These dreams seemed so real. I look forward to sleeping because maybe in sleeping I might see her. On the days following such a dream, I would replay it over and over in my mind, still smiling and humming to her the next morning. By afternoon, the activity and noise had usually worn the dream off.

I heard after the funeral that people were whispering and asking questions about what had happened. It didn't bother me. Nothing anyone said or did would bring my sweet baby back—that was clear. I never asked my daughter how it happened. After the baby's death, she and her husband became very quiet and they were together so much, they seemed like shadows of each other. Her husband worked at different jobs, and she just went with him and waited in the pickup until he was through. He worked with horses, helped build hooghans, corrals, and other construction work. When she came over and spent the afternoon with me, we hardly talked. We both knew we were more comfortable that way. As usual, she hugged me each time before she left. I knew she was in great pain.

Once, when I was at Basha's shopping for groceries, a woman I didn't know said to me, "You have a pretty grandbaby." I smiled and didn't reply. I noticed that she didn't say "*yée*" at the end of "*nitsóíh*" which would have meant "the grandbaby who is no longer alive." That happened at other places, and I didn't respond, except to smile. I thought it was good that people remembered her.

About four months after her death, we were eating at my house when my sisters gathered around me and told me they were very worried about me. They thought I was still too grief-stricken over the baby, and that it was not healthy. "You have to go on," they said, "let her go." They said they wanted the "old me" back, so I agreed to go for help.

We went to a medicine woman near Ganado, and she asked me if I could see the baby sometimes. No, I said, except in dreams.

"Has anyone said they've seen her?" she asked, I said that I didn't think so. Then she said, "Right, now, I see the baby beside you." I was so startled that I began looking around for her.

"The baby hasn't left," she said, "she wants to stay with you." I couldn't see my grandbaby. Then I realized that other people could see what the medicine woman had just seen. No wonder, I thought, that sometimes when I woke, I could feel her warm body beside me. She said the baby was wrapped in white.

She couldn't help me herself, but she told me to see another medicine person near Lukaichakai. She said that the ceremony I needed was very old and that she didn't know it herself. The man she recommended was elderly and very knowledgeable and so it was likely that he would know the ceremony, or would at least know of someone who did.

Early in the morning, we went to his house west of Many Farms—word had already been sent that we were coming. The ceremony lasted for four days and three nights, and parts of songs and prayers had such ancient sacred words I wasn't sure if I understood them. When the old man prayed and sang, sometimes tears streamed down my face as I repeated everything after him—word for word, line for line, late into the night—and we would begin again at daybreak the next morning. I was exhausted and so relieved. I finally realized what my grief had done. I could finally let my grandbaby go.

We were lucky that we had found this old man because the ceremony had not been done in almost eighty years. He had seen it as a little boy and had memorized all the parts of it—the songs, the advice, the prayers, and the literal letting go of the dead spirit. Over time, it has become a rare ceremony, because what I had done in holding and keeping the baby for those hours was not in keeping with the Navajo way. I understood that doing so had upset the balance of life and death. When we left, we were all crying. I thanked the old man for his memory, his life, and his ability to help us when no one else could. I understand now that all of life has ceremonies connected with it, and for us, without our memory, our old people, and our children, we would be like lost people in this world we live in, as well as in the other worlds in which our loved ones are waiting.

Responding Personally

1. To what does the title refer? Compare ideas with a partner.
2. Write about your own experiences in grieving for someone who was close to you.

Responding Critically

3. How was the narrator "hanging on" to the deceased baby? Did she know she was doing this? Explain.
4. In a small group, consider the following questions: By the end of the story, what has the grandmother learned about grieving? Has she resolved her conflict?
5. What cultural traditions are mentioned in the story's details? What does the story reveal about aboriginal ceremonies connected with the grieving process?
6. Given the initial topic of infant death, is the story finally optimistic or pessimistic in its tone? Compare your opinion with those of a classmate.

Responding Creatively

7. As the grandmother, write the lyrics for a song dedicated to your deceased granddaughter.
8. Compose a fairy tale or myth based on the same theme that is in this story.

Problem-Solving/Decision-Making

9. In a small group, brainstorm ideas about what a person can do to overcome depression from tragedy. What advice would you give to someone who had experienced a tragedy similar to the one in this story?

How did she know that the old man hadn't eaten?

Chi Li

Willow Waist

Translated by Scott W. Galer

The late-spring plum rains fell softly, sadly, lightly, silently. Dusk encroached everywhere; the sky was dark, the earth dizzy, everything near and far was completely dreary.

A small dreary street in a big dreary city.

A small eel-like sedan drifted up slowly.

Faint streetlamps were so far apart that the shadows of the few pedestrians out on the street were stretched taut. They swayed unsteadily. The superstitious driver slithered in and out like a snake, afraid of running over someone's shadow.

"What's the problem, Tian?" asked the old man in the backseat.

A bit put out, the driver replied, "What do you mean, 'What's the problem,' Mr. Guo? Are we there yet, sir?"

"You can park just up ahead."

"Hm," said the driver, as if relieved of a heavy burden.

The old man said, "You know I won't need a car anymore after this, don't you?"

The driver was rattled, "Mr. Guo, how can you say that? I can't stand it! I'm not one of those petty, opportunistic people who burn their bridges behind them! All these years you—"

"Stop the car," said the old man.

Not waiting for the driver to open the door, the old man stepped out, slammed the door shut behind him, and walked off.

The old man turned into a small alley.

The old man purposefully wound his way down the labyrinthine alley.

The old man stopped in front of a building with dappled walls. He sized up the building, which looked like an ancient Buddhist temple, reached out to touch the green moss between the bricks, and then rang the bell above the two huge China-fir doors.

The creaky door opened a crack. The entryway was dimly lit. The old fellow who opened the door recognized the guest in the dim light, stepped aside, then closed the squeaky door after the guest. Steam began hissing from two kettles at the same time. Both kettles lay atop charcoal stoves alongside two doors. Old men standing in the doorways stopped what they were doing and stared through rheumy eyes at the visitor climbing the stairs.

The stairway seemed darker and narrower than before. The banister was cold and smooth, like a frozen snake. The old man was forced to lean his paunchy body forward as he negotiated one step at a time. The steps creaked and groaned beneath the heavy weight. The sound of the old man's footsteps echoed through the foyer like the sound of a bell in a deserted valley. A shrill voice shattered the quiet from downstairs: "Who's that? Stop that devilish clomping, or you'll bring the house down! What did those poor stairs ever do to you?"

Ignoring the woman, the old man kept climbing, one step after another.

Suddenly, the stairway was illuminated. The old man raised his head and saw her. She stood at the top of the staircase, thoughtfully shining a flashlight on the steps beneath the old man's feet.

He reached the top of the stairs. She looked up at him and remarked tenderly, "You've come."

The old man said, "Yes, I have."

The old man felt relaxed, like a bird returning to its nest, as if he came here every day.

She followed him into the room, leaving the door unlatched.

The winter warming stove hadn't yet been put away; on it sat a steaming earthenware kettle. The dark-blue flames danced playfully at the base of the kettle. The small room was warmer than early summer. The faint smell of sandalwood incense hung in the air. A small light above the stove formed a halo of light around the stove. The rest of the room was dark and shadowy.

In the dark shadows, she took off the once costly woolen coat that she wore when she went out, revealing a black, narrow-sleeved thin cotton jacket. Oh, her waist was still hourglass thin. Even at her age.

The old man gazed at her.

She took the old man's hat and shook the fine droplets of rain off the woolen surface, saying, "Oh, these spring rains."

Then with a dry towel, she gently dried off the old man's clothes, from his collar to his pant legs.

She moved two faded old-fashioned armchairs up to the stove. "Sit down," she said, "I'll make some tea."

The old man sat down. Amid the delicate fragrance of the warm, dry heat, the old man felt completely relaxed; his joints cracked as they loosened up.

She carried over a serving tray and removed the tea towel covering it. On the tray were an Yixing ceramic teapot, two ceramic teacups, and a ceramic jar. After warming the teapot with hot water, she scooped a few spoonfuls of tea leaves out of the ceramic jar with an ivory teaspoon and put them into the teapot. She then refilled the teapot with hot water and put the lid on tightly. After a moment, she lifted up the water bottle and poured hot water over the outside of the teapot. The reddish-purple color of the ceramic teaware and the pair of small, pale, bony hands looked like a flower of unmatched beauty slowly blossoming. She prepared the tea with composure, her hands and eyes in perfect accord, completely absorbed in the task.

The aroma of the tea seeped out.

After pouring a cup of tea for the old man, she took out a plate of his favorite treats, long famous in the small alleys of the big city: crab cakes. A habit of many years it was for the old man to enjoy this treat only if he hadn't already eaten.

She poured herself half a cup of tea and sat down across from the old man, separated from him by the stove.

How did she know that the old man hadn't eaten?

Did she know why the old man had walked away from the dinner table?

Did she know that the old man had already retired?

Did she know that the old man had decided to move out of the small red building?

Did she know that because of all this, the old man's children had attacked him?

Did she know that his wife was prepared to fight to the death to retain the small red building?

Did she know of the looks of resentment in the eyes of the two domestics who served him his meals?

Did she know that the quiet, soft-spoken driver of many years had begun saying things to distance himself?

And even more awful things—did she know of them? That would be …

"I was afraid you might not have had dinner. Take the edge off your hunger with these snacks," she said. She looked at the old man, smiled, and took a sip of tea. She knew it all.

The old man felt transparent: he was a mass of agitation and anger. Was it necessary to tell every little detail?

Her knees were together, her feet side by side. Narrow shoulders, a slender waist, delicate fingers, a warm expression of quiet humility—as she sat with an air of quaint antiquity, her warm, peaceful humility flowed endlessly toward the old man.

The old man's frustration and anger gradually subsided.

Separated only by the stove, they gazed at each other in silence, using their beating hearts to read the history of each new wrinkle on each other's face.

The old man's face was crisscrossed with ravines.

The skin on her face had folds in length and breadth.

An abstruse heavenly tome that only the two of them could understand.

Suddenly, it dawned upon the old man that her hair had turned white. Puzzled, he wondered when it was that the last strand of black hair had disappeared.

Silently, she shook her head, releasing waves of silvery light.

Why should he be puzzled? The first strand of hair turns white, and so does the last one. What's so special about one's hair turning white? It would be strange if hair that had grown for so many years did not turn white; a person isn't truly old until the hair turns white. Her white hair was like snow, her face was like snow, kindly and yet noble. The dimple on her left cheek appeared as a hollow spot on the surface of that snow created by a hot teardrop. Therein lay the essence of old-fashioned feminine beauty. So why be sad over white hair?

The old man understood.

The tea mellowed on the second brewing. They sat facing each other without a word or a sound.

Oh, her waist was still hourglass thin. Even at her age.

Yes, she's old now. Time flies like an arrow; everyone grows old. What's so special about growing old? How boring life would be without change.

What is there to be sorry about? What else do you have? In the end, what does anyone have? Doesn't everyone come into the world naked and leave the same way? How pleasant that the stove is so warm tonight, the tea steeped so well, and that you and I can still drink a cup together.

She took a sip of tea.

The old man took a sip of tea.

The gloomy look on the old man's face vanished, replaced by a spreading glow. He was at peace, refreshed.

They sat, and they sat, and they sat, a hint of happiness and joy occasionally flickering across their stony faces.

The dark-blue flames were no longer dancing. The coals in the stove were completely red, burning silently. The rolling steam atop the kettle turned to white smoke and curled upward.

Was that a cat or a person outside? Tiptoeing back and forth, then stopping just outside the door for a long time before walking on.

The tea weakened considerably on the third brewing. The old man stood up and paced the floor. Each piece of furniture was where it had always been; only the colors had darkened—spotlessly clean, but already the color of death. The sandalwood incense had burned out; the ashes had fallen to the floor. The smell of mildew emerged from the four corners of the room. It was the old, rotten sort of mildew that the sun could not burn off or shine through.

The old man was reminded of something. He asked, "Did this flare up again?" He pointed to his heart.

Without turning her head to look, she answered clearly, "Twice, both times in the winter, and both times I was hospitalized."

The old man said, "I had two attacks, too, also in the winter, and I was hospitalized. We're the same." The old man laughed like a child. She smiled.

"Well, I should be going," said the old man.

She rose slowly and picked up his hat. The old man leaned forward and lowered his head; she stood on tiptoes to place the hat properly on the old man's head.

Oh, her waist was still hourglass thin.

The old man put his hands on the slender waist. "I'm no longer an official. I can finally relax."

"You should be going," she said.

The old man's grasp loosened, He was secretly ashamed. Had she not stopped him so quickly he might have broken his word.

In the dark shadows, she put on her once costly woolen coat and tied a scarf over her head. Looking like a baby in swaddling clothes, she raised her wrinkled forehead and said, "Come again if you have time."

The old man turned back and looked at that stove, at the old-fashioned armchairs, and at the two nearly empty teacups. Then he looked into her calm, quiet, humble eyes and said, "All right."

She escorted the old man to the front door, curling up inside the doorway.

The old man stopped, turned, and waved her back inside. She stayed for a moment, then retreated; the shiny black door creaked.

In the instant before the two doors met, the old man thought he saw a single teardrop ooze through the crack.

The old man hurried back to where he had been and touched the spot where the tear had emerged; it was wet. He touched his finger to the tip of his tongue and tasted it. Salty and sweet at the same time. When he touched it again, the whole door was wet. The plum rains were still falling, softly and sadly.

The fog turned the alley vast and hazy; the fog turned the street vast and hazy; the fog turned the boulevard vast and hazy. The outlines of tall buildings were blurred; dark shadows were everywhere; lights in homes were dim as starlight. The sky and the earth fused at the horizon, misty and blurred, a ball of chaos. Even if you were a good son, how could you clear away the clouds and fog and stop the wind and rain to seek a sky you yourself loved? No, let nature take its course; nature is fair, so why must we seek things by force?

Take a step back; the sea and sky are boundless.

The old man said to the driver in an unusually calm tone, "I've made you wait too long."

Responding Personally

1. Does the ending turn out differently than you thought it would? Explain.
2. Is it possible for two people not married to one another to be closely attached to each other over a long period of time? Explain.

Responding Critically

3. What is the purpose of the last four paragraphs? What do they add to the story?
4. For small group discussion: What kinds of troubles does the old man have? How is he "caught in a trap"? What does the fact that the woman knows about these troubles suggest about their relationship?

5. For paragraph response: Why do you think their relationship has gone on for so long without the old man leaving his unhappy life behind and joining her? Do you think the old man and woman are well-matched? Explain.
6. The story has a strong setting and atmosphere. Quote three images from the story that create a vivid sense of time and place.

Responding Creatively

7. Compose a haiku the old man might give to the woman. Compare your finished poem to ones written by classmates.
8. With a partner, prepare a photo essay on the elderly. Display it on a class bulletin board.

Problem-Solving/Decision-Making

9. Suppose the old man decides to leave his family and marry the old woman. Write the conversation he and the woman have when he makes his marriage proposal.

Glossary of Fiction Terms

allusion
An allusion is a brief direct or indirect reference to a person, place, or event from history, literature, or mythology that the author hopes or assumes the reader will recognize. Most allusions expand on or develop a significant idea, impression, or mood in the story. "The Veldt" contains allusions to literary characters such as Rima from *Green Mansions*, in order to suggest the rich, imaginative powers of the nursery.

antagonist
The antagonist is the major character or force that opposes the protagonist. In "The Carved Table," Karen, the protagonist, finds herself opposed to her husband's family, who become the antagonists.

antecedent action
This is the significant action that takes place before the story begins. In "The Persian Carpet," the antecedent action is the flashback to the rug theft.

anticlimax
An anticlimax is a sudden shift from a relatively serious or elevated mood to one more comic or trivial. The humorous September 11th entry in "Barney" is an example of anticlimax after the previous serious entries by the scientist.

antihero
An antihero is a protagonist who has none of the qualities normally expected of a hero. The term also refers to a humorous take-off of the traditional hero. The characters played by Woody

Allen and Rowan Atkinson (Mr. Bean) are examples of antiheroes. In "The Third or Fourth Happiest Man in Nova Scotia," Ray is a comical "loser" antihero who tends wounded birds and animals.

atmosphere (or mood)

The atmosphere or mood is the prevailing feeling created by the story. Atmosphere usually sets up expectations in the reader about the outcome of an episode or plot. It is created by descriptive diction, imagery, and sometimes dialogue. Some teachers or critics may distinguish between the two terms by referring to the "atmosphere of a story" and the "mood created in the reader." The atmosphere in "The Dress" is tense, reflecting the conflict between mother and daughter.

character

The term refers to both a fictional person in a story, and the moral, dispositional, and behavioural qualities of that fictional person. The qualities of a character are generally revealed through dialogue, action, and description. Characters themselves may be classified as flat or round, stereotyped or realistic, static or dynamic. Each classification is described below. See also *foil.*

Classifications of Character

- *Flat character* is a limited, usually minor character with only one apparent quality. The various characters in "Sculpin" are sketchily drawn flat characters.
- *Round character* is a realistic character with several dimensions. The grandfather in "Flight" is a round character developed in some detail.
- *Realistic character* is a multi-dimensional and recognizable character who has complex relationships and motivations. Carolee in "A Television Drama" is a realistically portrayed housewife.
- *Stereotyped character* is a predictable, one-dimensional character who is recognizable to the reader as "of a type," for example, the jock, the brain, the yuppie. Karen's father-in-law in "The Carved Table" is a stereotype of the loud, hard-drinking materialist.

- *Dynamic character* is often the protagonist and is a character who undergoes a significant, lasting change, usually in his or her outlook on life. In "Death of a Snow Machine," Skeeptoe is a dynamic character who abandons technology in favour of the old transportation method of a dog-team.
- *Static character* is one who does not change in the course of the story. The mother in "The Dress" is a difficult person to live with who is not likely to change.

characterization

Characterization is the process through which the author reveals to the reader the qualities of a character. In short stories, the author will either reveal character directly (through author comments) and/or indirectly (through the character's speech, thoughts, or actions).

character sketch

A character sketch is a description and analysis of a character's moral, dispositional, and behavioural qualities, including specific examples and quotations from the story. When writing a character sketch, one does not normally describe the character's physical appearance or dress, though these, incidentally, may reflect symbolically the character's personality. A character sketch for Johnny's father in "The Father" is the following:

> In "The Father," Johnny's father is portrayed as an insensitive boor who repeatedly exhibits poor judgement and constantly embarrasses his son. For instance, he says to the scoutmaster that taking Johnny to a burlesque show would have been a better use of the ticket money. Later, he gets drunk and raises his son's hand "like a referee signifying the winner of a boxing bout," then knocks a vase and plates onto the floor.
>
> Throughout the story, he also reveals his ignorance and an overconfident casualness which finally leads to a major separation between himself and the boy. For example, on the way to the banquet, he reveals his lack of knowledge about Johnny's friends and his baseball activities. Arrogantly, he assumes he is

better than the other scout fathers and thinks that Johnny will love, respect, and forgive him despite his errors. At the conclusion, the father learns too late that he has acted foolishly and irresponsibly, and that he may have permanently damaged the relationship between himself and Johnny: "he wondered if he would ever be able to draw close to his son again."

climax

The climax is the highest point of emotional intensity in a story. It is the major crisis in the story and usually marks the turning point in the protagonist's fortunes. The climax in "The Friday Everything Changed" occurs when Miss Ralston hits a home run.

complicating incident (or complication)

The event that initiates a conflict is the complicating incident. In "The Sea Devil," the man's solitary night-fishing leading to the conflict with the ray is the complicating incident.

confidant (or confidante)

The confidant(e) is the person with whom a character, usually the protagonist, shares his or her thoughts, feelings, and intentions. The little sister in "Alicia" is the confidante of her mad older sister.

conflict

This term refers to the struggle between opposing characters or forces, that is, the protagonist and someone or something else. Additional conflicts, which the protagonist is not involved in, may also be found in a short story. Three common types of conflicts are as follows:

1. *Conflict between a character and his or her environment.* The environment may be nature, society, or circumstance. In "The Sea Devil," the man's solitary night-fishing leads to the conflict with the ray. In "A Mountain Journey," Dave Conroy is in conflict with the cold rugged terrain that stands between him and rescue.

2. *Conflict between two characters.* This struggle may be physical, emotional, or psychological. The narrator in "The Persian Carpet" is in conflict with her mother who has blamed an innocent man for a phantom theft.
3. *Conflict within a character.* In this case, the character experiences conflict in emotion and/or thought. Mrs. Evans in "A Little Beaded Bag" has mixed feelings toward her husband and the maid who has taken her handbag.

contrast (or juxtaposition)

Contrast refers to a difference, especially a striking difference, between two things being compared. In this context, contrast may involve characters, situations, settings, moods, or points of view. Contrast is used in order to clarify meaning, purpose, or character, or to heighten certain moods (especially humour, horror, and suspense).

In "A Penny in the Dust," there is a contrast between Pete's private dream for his father and the father's incorrect assumption that his son feared being beaten for losing the penny.

Juxtapositions are contrasts in which positioning is important, for example, when two contrasting characters are placed side-by-side in a story. An interesting juxtaposition of characters occurs in "The Duel" when the sorrowful friend is trying to tell the cheerful mother the news that her son is dead.

crisis

A crisis is a moment of intense conflict. The major crisis of the story is called the climax.

In "The Dress," a crisis occurs when the mother barges into her spinster-daughter's conversation with a travelling saleswoman about buying a dress.

denouement (or resolution)

Denouement (pronounced day-NEW-mahn) is the French word for "unknotting" and refers to the unknotting of or resolution to the plot or conflict. The denouement follows the climax and constitutes part or all of the falling action. The denouement in "Willow Waist" occurs when Mr. Guo leaves the building where his friend lives.

dialect

Dialect is a manner of speaking or variation on a language peculiar to an individual, a people, a social class, or a geographic region. A dialect differs from the standard language of a country. In "All the Colors of Sunset," the grandmother speaks Navajo dialect: "I asked her, "*Nits'iiyah sha'*?"

dialogue

Any conversation between two or more characters in a story is dialogue. In "Call Me," the telephone messages and callers' responses are an interesting approach to dialogue.

diction

Diction is the vocabulary used by a writer. For each story, the writer chooses and arranges words appropriate to his or her purpose, subject, story type, characters, and style. In "Willow Waist," very sparse diction is used—for example, "The creaky door opened a crack. The entryway was dimly lit"—to suggest the simplicity of the setting and characters.

dilemma

A dilemma is a situation in which a character must make a choice between two disagreeable, undesirable, or unfavourable alternatives. Posing a dilemma is one method an author can use to generate conflict and suspense in a story.

In "The Old Woman," Florrie has to make a choice between avoiding contact with Mrs. Cornish altogether, which will lead to an increase in the latter's loneliness and isolation, or allowing herself to continue as the old woman's confidante and protector, at the expense of an independent life for herself.

dynamic character
See *character.*

epiphany
Epiphany refers to a moment of significant realization and insight experienced by the protagonist, often at the end of a story. As a literary term, epiphany originates with James Joyce, who built each short story in his *Dubliners* around what he called an epiphany. An epiphany in "The Whale" occurs when Ambroise realizes that Gabrielle loves him despite thinking he is lying to impress her.

episode
An episode is an incident or event within the main plot of the story. Episodes can be viewed as selected portions or scenes developed in detail by the author. The phone messages in "Call Me" form a series of episodes, tracing the relationship of Shawna and George.

escapist fiction
This refers to stories written solely to entertain the reader, thus helping the reader to escape the daily cares and problems of reality. While provoking thought on the part of the reader and providing entertainment for the reader are not mutually exclusive, the term escapist fiction suggests an extreme. Escapist fiction has lively melodramatic plots and stereotyped or flat characters, and it requires limited involvement on the part of the reader. Many mass-marketed science fiction, westerns, thrillers, and romances fall into the category of escapist fiction.

"Barney" comes closest to being classified as escapist fiction in this book.

exposition
Exposition is background information provided by the author to further the development of plot, conflict, setting, and characterization. The first four paragraphs of "Sculpin" present exposition about life in a particular Newfoundland seaport.

falling action

The falling action is the action immediately following the climax and lasting until the end of the story. In "The Sea Devil," the events following the man's severing the rope to free himself from the ray is falling action.

fantasy

A fantasy is a highly exaggerated or improbable story. As a rule, fantasy has fantastic events, characters, and/or settings not found in real life. "Barney" is a fantasy about an intelligence experiment gone wrong.

fiction

Fiction is any narrative which is imagined or invented. Fiction may be based on actual happenings, which can, in turn, make fiction seem realistic.

flashback

A flashback is a sudden switch in the plot from the present to the past. This device may be used to illustrate an important point or to aid in characterization. In "The Persian Carpet," the protagonist recalls the day the carpet was supposedly stolen.

flat character

See *character.*

foil

A foil is a character whose behaviour, attitudes, and/or opinions contrast with those of the protagonist. The contrast of the foil helps the reader to understand better the character and motivation of the protagonist. In "Flight," the coolness of the mother makes her a foil to the anxious, unhappy grandfather.

foreshadowing

This is a device which hints or warns of events to happen later in the story. Foreshadowing prepares the reader for the climax, the denouement, and any changes in the protagonist. In "Alicia," the mad sister's biting of the young protagonist foreshadows her increasing violence and descent into insanity.

form

Form is a general term referring to the way in which a story is put together, its shape or structure. Form is sometimes called the "how" of a story, and includes both technique and style. The form of "Call Me" is a combination of recipient and caller telephone messages.

goal

See *motivation.*

hero (or heroine)

This is a protagonist of a story who possesses heroic qualities such as courage, or virtues such as honesty. The terms *hero* and *heroine* are not interchangeable with the more general term *protagonist.* The man in "The Sea Devil" is a hero because he overcomes the ray with his resourcefulness, intelligence, and daring.

humour

Humour refers to writing that is intended to amuse the reader or provoke laughter. "The Third or Fourth Happiest Man in Nova Scotia" is a humorous character profile.

images (and imagery)

Images are concrete details and figures of speech that help the reader form vivid impressions of the subject. Imagery refers to the pattern of images in a single piece of writing. "The Empty Frame" uses images such as the following to achieve horror: "The earth began to absorb blood. All the *karez,* wells, and springs began to sprout blood."

indeterminate ending

A story ending in which there is no clear outcome, result, or resolved conflict is called an indeterminate ending. "The Carved

Table" has an indeterminate ending, with the reader not knowing what Karen will do next.

in medias res

In medias res (pronounced in MA-deas RAS) is a Latin term which refers to readers joining a story "in the middle of things." "Aero Bars" joins the story in progress, with the father receiving hospital treatments for cancer.

interpretive fiction

This term refers to stories which have meaningful, usually realistic, plots, conflicts, settings, and characters. Interpretive fiction is usually serious in tone and designed to be interpreted. It is instructive, unlike escapist fiction, which is designed chiefly for entertainment. Most of the stories in this text are examples of interpretive fiction.

irony

Irony involves contrast between two elements and, as a literary device, provides depth of meaning and impact. When irony is used, meanings tend to become unconcealed or contradictory, an effect which we call "ironic." The following are three common types of irony:

1. *Verbal irony* occurs when what a character says contrasts with what the character actually means. In "A Little Beaded Bag," when Mrs. Evans suggests that the maid fix the purse for herself, she is really apologizing to the girl and asking for forgiveness.
2. *Dramatic irony* occurs when what a character says or believes contrasts with what the reader or other characters know to be true, based on information given to us by the author. In "The Duel," the dead man's mother assumes the friend has come to pay a social visit, not knowing he brings news her son is dead.
3. *Situational irony* (or irony of situation) occurs when what finally takes place is different from what was expected or seemed appropriate. In "A Little Beaded Bag," Mrs. Evans

ends up giving her maid the handbag after the latter had stolen and returned it.

juxtaposition
See *contrast.*

local colour (and regionalism)
Local colour refers to the detail in a story that is specific to a geographic region or an environment. Local colour develops the setting and atmosphere, increases reader interest, and adds to authenticity by including descriptions of locale, dress, customs, dialect, and ways of thinking and feeling characteristic of local people. Regionalism refers to stories in which setting (developed with local colour) is of significance to the text and necessary to the writer's purpose. Regionalism is obvious in the description of setting found in "Afrika Road."

In "The Friday Everything Changed," the details of a baseball game in a small post-World War II school in Atlantic Canada would be an example of local colour.

mood
See *atmosphere.*

moral
The implied lesson of a story is called the moral. Viewed in isolation, a moral is a relatively unimportant part of a story and should not be confused with theme, a far more significant element of fiction. A moral for "The Veldt" might be that parents shouldn't spoil their children.

motivation (and goal)
Motivation is both what causes a character to do what he or she does and the character's aim, or goal, in taking that action. The character's temperament and circumstances determine motivation. The pursuit by the protagonist of his or her goal results in the story's conflict. Characters must have sufficient and plausible

motivation in order for a reader to find the story effective. The motivation of the protagonist in "Cancer" is to get attention.

narrative

Narrative is another word for "story." Narratives contain the following elements: plot, conflict, characters, setting, and point of view. Narratives may be fictional or non-fictional, and include novels, autobiographies, biographies, short stories, and anecdotes.

narrator

The narrator is the storyteller. In the case of a story told from the first person perspective, the narrator is one of the characters; in the case of a story told from the objective, omniscient, or limited omniscient points of view, the author assumes the role of narrator.

In "Penny in the Dust," the adult Pete is the narrator.

plot

The storyline or organization of events or episodes within a story is called the plot. The conventional plot has rising action, a climax, and falling action. See also *subplot*.

point of view

The point of view is the perspective from which a story is seen or told. Point of view establishes the relationships among author, reader, and characters. The following are the three most common points of view:

1. *First-person narrative* features a character telling the story directly to the reader in the first person (that is, using "I"). This point of view tells us what the character thinks and feels from a vantage point "inside" the story, from one character's perspective. "Wild Horses" uses a first-person narrative.
2. *Limited omniscient* or third-person narrative occurs when a story is told from "outside" the characters, but from the perspective of one character. In this point of view, the characters are referred to in the third person (as "he" or "she"), and

the narrator is limited to knowing the thoughts and feelings of only that one character. "The Dress" uses a limited omniscient narrative.

3. *Omniscient narrative* or "all-knowing" narrative tells the story with knowledge of the thoughts and feelings of more than one, or all the characters. "Sculpin" uses a God-like omniscient narrative.

predicament

A predicament is a difficult problem or unpleasant situation. Predicament should not be confused with a related term, *dilemma* (see above). In "A Television Drama," Carolee deals with the predicament of having a criminal on the run from the police in her immediate neighbourhood.

prose

Ordinary language or literary expression not marked by obvious rhythm or rhyme is called prose. This type of language is used in short stories, essays, and modern plays. The text you are now reading is written in prose.

protagonist

The protagonist is the main character of a story. While some protagonists may be heroes or heroines (or antiheroes and antiheroines), the term protagonist is broader and does not depend on moral judgements of the character's actions. The protagonist of "All the Colors of Sunset" is the grandmother.

purpose

Purpose refers to the main effect the author hopes to achieve, for example, entertainment, thought, enlightenment, action, demonstrating something about life or human nature. Rarely does a story have only one purpose. Purpose may include theme, but should not simply be equated with the story's main idea. One purpose of "Willow Waist" is to explore a special, long-standing clandestine relationship.

realism

This term refers to any subject matter or techniques that create a true-to-life impression for the reader. Writers of realism present life "as it is" and as though the stories have simply "told themselves." In another sense, realism can also refer to stories about simple, everyday people. See also *fantasy, romance,* and *verisimilitude.*

"Call Me" captures the realism of people's inability to communicate despite the use of modern technology.

realistic character

See *character.*

regionalism

See *local colour.* Significant use of regionalism occurs in "A Mountain Journey" when the mountainous Canadian terrain creates various obstacles during Dave Conroy's flight to shelter.

resolution

See *denouement.*

rising action

Rising action in a story consists of the incidents that precede the climax. During this stage of the story, background information is given, characters and conflicts are introduced, and suspense is built up. There may even be moments of crisis. Typically, the rising action is often longer than the falling action of a story. See also *plot.* In "Death of a Snow Machine," the long section before the protagonist shoots the snowmobile constitutes the rising action.

romance

Entertaining stories that contain one or more of the following characteristics—fantasy, improbability, extravagance, naiveté, love, adventure, myth—are generally called romances. "Willow Waist" is an example of a romance with an emphasis on adventure.

round character

See *character.*

satire

Satire is the use of irony to ridicule an idea, a person, or a thing, often with an aim to provoke change. Satire usually targets human foibles or vices. "Death of a Snow Machine" is a satire intended to suggest that aboriginal peoples would be better off following the old ways rather than those of technology.

science fiction

Science fiction is speculative writing about the effects of technology or science on the future of human beings. While the purpose of some science fiction is purely escapist entertainment, science fiction can be written for a range of serious purposes, too. "Barney" is an example of science fiction.

setting

The setting is the time and place of a story. While, in some stories, setting may affect the plot, conflict, characters, and theme, in others, it can be of great significance and the main fiction element. In "The Veldt," the extraordinary nursery implies a futuristic setting.

short story

A short story is a brief fictional prose narrative, having one main character, a single plot, limited setting, and one main effect. Edgar Allan Poe, one of the first significant theorists and practitioners of short story writing, said that short stories:

1. can be read in one sitting, and derive their power from the fact the writer has to select details for economy and emphasis
2. have a single effect or purpose and are constructed so that every sentence from the first to the last one supports that effect
3. leave the reader with a feeling of satisfaction and finality, desiring no further completion or alternate ending
4. have their basis in truth or life-likeness.

static character
See *character.*

stereotype
A stereotype is any fixed pattern of plot or character. Stereotyped plots usually fall into the realm of escapist fiction. Stereotyped characters are familiar figures in fiction, such as the hard-boiled private investigator, the absent-minded professor, or the military officer with a stiff upper lip. See also *character.* In "A Mountain Journey," Dave Conroy represents the stereotype of the overconfident man who fails to survive, a pattern echoed in other works such as Jack London's "To Build a Fire."

stream of consciousness
Stream of consciousness is a modern narrative technique that attempts to depict the uninterrupted flow of feelings and random thoughts of a character's mind. However, the author includes details relevant to plot, character, and theme in the apparently natural flow of thoughts and feelings.

In "The Carved Table," there are sections using the stream of consciousness technique, for example, Karen's flow of thoughts—"We have nuclear weapons. We need a different set of rules."

style
Style is the individual manner in which an author expresses himself or herself. In fiction, style is basically determined by such grammatical and sensory aspects as diction, sentences, and images.

"Call Me" is written as a combination of recipient and caller telephone messages.

subplot
A subplot is a minor storyline, secondary to the main plot. Subplots may be related or unrelated to the main action, but may also be a reflection of, or variation on, the main plot. Compared to novels, short stories tend to have few, brief subplots (or none) because of the brevity and density required of the short story

genre. A subplot of "Flight" is the struggle between the old man and his daughter for control over his granddaughter.

surprise ending

The sudden twist in the direction of a story, producing a resolution that surprises the reader and often the story's characters as well, is called a surprise ending. In "Barney," the surprise ending comes when the reader realizes that Barney is writing the last entry.

suspense

Suspense is the feeling of anxiety and uncertainty experienced by the reader (and possibly characters) about the outcome of events or the protagonist's fate. In "The Empty Frame," there is suspense building up to the doctor's actually viewing the mad patient's picture.

symbol

A symbol is something that stands for or represents something else. Characters, objects, events, conflicts, and settings can all be symbolic. "Aero Bars" uses the symbol of a chocolate bar as a personal link between father and son, and as a sign of their long-term love for each other.

theme

The theme is the central idea of the story, usually implied rather than directly stated. It is a story's observation about life or human nature, and should never be confused with the moral. The theme of "The Father" is that parents, through ignorance and insensitivity, can alienate themselves from their children.

thematic statement

This is a one sentence general statement about life or human nature that can be derived by interpreting a story's overall message. It does not mention specifics from the story (that is, specific names, settings, or events), but instead generalizes accurately and comprehensively about the story's main meaning. A thematic statement for "The Father" might be as follows: Parents, through ignorance and insensitivity, can alienate themselves from their children.

universality

Universality is the quality of a story that gives it relevance beyond the narrow confines of its particular characters, subject, or setting. Stories which have universality reveal human nature or common truths of life experience. Universality in a story also implies that the story could apply to most people's experience. "The Persian Carpet" deals with the universal ideas that the truth will eventually come out and that innocent people are often blamed for others' greed and thoughtlessness.

verisimilitude

Verisimilitude is a life-like quality possessed by a story as revealed through its plot, setting, conflict, and characterization. See also *realism*. "The Old Woman" has a verisimilitude that apartment dwellers or people with elderly, nosy neighbours would best understand and appreciate.

vicarious experience

Vicarious experience refers to the reader sharing imaginatively in a character's feelings and experiences. Vicariously (literally, "acting or done for another") experiences can be had, for example, through reading travel literature. At the banquet in "The Father," the reader vicariously feels Johnny's humiliation in response to his father's behaviour.

Permission Credits

Every reasonable effort has been made to acquire permission for copyright material used in this text, and to acknowledge such indebtedness accurately. Any errors or omissions called to the publisher's attention will be corrected in future printings. In particular, we would be grateful for any information regarding the copyright holders of *Barney* by Will Stanton, and *Death of a Snow Machine* by Alfred Groulx.

The Persian Carpet by Hanan Shaykh, from ARABIC SHORT STORIES, translated by Denys Johnson-Davies. © 1983 by Denys Johnson-Davies. By permission of University of California Press. *The Friday Everything Changed* by Anne Hart. Reprinted by permission of the author. *Wild Horses* by Brian Fawcett, from MY CAREER WITH THE LEAFS AND OTHER STORIES, published by Talon Books Ltd. © 1982 Brian Fawcett. Reprinted by permission of Talon Books Ltd. *The Sea Devil* by Arthur Gordon, from THROUGH MANY WINDOWS by Arthur Gordon. © 1983 by Arthur Gordon. By permission of the author. *The Carved Table* by Mary Peterson. Reprinted by permission of the author. *Alicia* by Gabrielle Roy. From STREET OF RICHES, edited by Gabrielle Roy. Copyright © Fonds Gabrielle Roy. Used by permission of Fonds Gabrielle Roy. *The Father* by Hugh Garner. From HUGH GARNER'S SHORT STORIES, published by McGraw-Hill Ryerson. © Hugh Garner. Used by permission of McGraw-Hill Ryerson. *The Old Woman* by Elizabeth Brewster is reprinted from VISITATIONS by permission of Oberon Press. *A Mountain Journey* by Howard O'Hagan. © 1977 Howard O'Hagan. From THE WOMAN WHO GOT ON AT JASPER STATION by Howard O'Hagan. Used by permission of Talon Books Ltd. *Afrika Road* by Don Mattera. From

THE STORYTELLER by Don Mattera published 1993 and 1994 by Justified Press and 1991 by Farrar, Straus & Giroux. Reprinted by permission of the author. *The Veldt* by Ray Bradbury. Reprinted by permission of Don Congdon Associates, Inc. Copyright © 1950 by Curtis Publishing Co., renewed 1977 Ray Bradbury. *Penny in the Dust* by Ernest Buckler. Reprinted by permission of Curtis Brown New York. *A Little Beaded Bag* by Morley Callaghan. From THE LOST AND FOUND STORIES OF MORLEY CALLAGHAN, published by Lester & Orpen Dennys, © 1985 by Morley Callaghan. Reprinted by permission of the author's Estate. *Sculpin* by Tom Dawe, from BAFFLES OF WIND AND TIDE: A SELECTION OF NEWFOUNDLAND WRITING, edited by Clyde Rose, © 1974 Clyde Rose. Published with the permission of Breakwater, St. John's, copyright the author. *The Duel* by Nicolai Teleshov, from RUSSIAN SHORT STORIES, copyright © 1955 Studio Editions Ltd. Reprinted by permission of Studio Editions Ltd. *Flight* by Doris Lessing. Copyright © 1957 Doris Lessing. Reprinted by kind permission of Jonathan Clowes Ltd., London on behalf of Doris Lessing. *A Television Drama* by Jane Rule. Copyright © 1975 by Jane Rule. Reprinted with permission of Georges Borchardt, Inc. for the author. *The Whale* by Yves Thériault, from LA BLEINE, translated by Patricia Sillers, © 1981, published by VLB Editeur. Reprinted by permission of Succession Yves Thériault. *The Empty Frame* by Khalil Bawar, translated from Pashto by Ali Qumail Qizalbash and Asif Farrukhi. From FIRES IN THE AUTUMN GARDEN: SHORT STORIES FROM URDU AND THE REGIONAL LANGUAGES OF PAKISTAN, edited by Asif Farrukhi, Oxford University Press, Karachi, 1997. Reprinted by permission of Oxford University Press, Pakistan. *Call Me* by Judy McCrosky, from BRIDGE CITY ANTHOLOGY: STORIES FROM SASKATOON, published by Fifth House, © 1991. Reprinted by permission of the author. *Cancer* by Janice Deal. From OTHER VOICES 19 (Fall 1993), reprinted with permission of Other Voices Literary Magazine. *Aero Bars* by Robert Hilles. From NEAR MORNING by Robert Hilles, published by Black Moss Press, © 1995 Robert Hilles. Reprinted by permission of Black Moss Press. *The Dress* by Marta Jara. From WHAT IS SECRET? STORIES BY CHILEAN

WOMEN, edited by Marjorie Agosin. © 1995 Marjorie Agosin. Reprinted by permission of White Pine Press. *The Third or Fourth Happiest Man in Nova Scotia* by Lesley Choyce. From DANCE THE ROCKS ASHORE by Lesley Choyce (Goose Lane Editions, 1997). Reprinted by permission of the publisher. *All the Colors of Sunset* by Luci Tapahonso. From BLUE MESA REVIEW, copyright © 1994 by Luci Tapahonso, reprinted by permission of the author. *Willow Waist* by Chi Li, translated by Scott W. Galer, from CHAIRMAN MAO WOULD NOT BE AMUSED, edited by Howard Goldblatt. Copyright © 1992 by Chi Li, English translation copyright © 1995 by Scott W. Galer, used by permission of Grove/Atlantic, Inc.

Photo Credits

Abbreviations: t = top; c = centre; b = bottom; l = left; r = right

p. v (t) Birgitte Nielsen, (c) Jeremy Jones, (b) Dick Hemingway; p. vi (t) Birgitte Nielsen, (cl) Birgitte Nielsen, (cr) Jeremy Jones, (b) Dick Hemingway; p. vii Matthew Wienreb/Image Bank; p. x Birgitte Nielsen; p. 3 Birgitte Nielsen; p. 14 Vicky Kasala/Image Bank; p. 24 Jeremy Jones; p. 28 Birgitte Nielsen; p. 34 Jeff Hunter/Image Bank; p. 46 Image Bank; p. 50 Dick Hemingway; p. 54 Birgitte Nielsen; p. 78 Comstock; p. 96 Birgitte Nielsen; p. 100 Pat Bates/Tony Stone Images; p. 109 Mark Douet/Tony Stone Images; p. 116 Pete Turner/Image Bank; p. 132 Birgitte Nielsen; p. 134 Birgitte Nielsen; p. 147 Brian Sytnyk/Masterfile; p. 154 Jeremy Jones; p. 162 Wayne Bilenduke/Tony Stone Images; p. 168 James Darell/Tony Stone Images; p. 176 Dick Hemingway; p. 185 Art Wolfe/Tony Stone Images; p. 192 Pat Lacroix/Image Bank; p. 198 Matthew Weinreb/Image Bank; p. 223 Yuri Dojc/Image Bank; p. 230 Peter Gridley/FPG/Masterfile.